# DEEP
## MEDICINE

# DEEP
## MEDICINE

*William B. Stewart, M.D.*

**Foreword by Angeles Arrien, Ph.D.**

*Deep Medicine*

Library of Congress Cataloging-in-Publication Data

Stewart, William B.
    Deep Medicine/William B. Stewart. P.cm.
    Includes bibliographical references
    ISBN I-58151-085-3
  1.  Health—Philosophy. 2. Mind and Body. I. Title.

RA776.5.S8145  2001
613'.01—dc21
2001016139

Printed in Dexter, Michigan by Thomson-Shore, Inc.

# Dedication

*With deep gratitude this book is dedicated to the Medicine that has been passed down from our ancestors across the globe. It is my sincere wish that these words will help bridge ancient practices with modern medicine for the benefit of generations yet to come. As each of us becomes more healthy, more whole, we can contribute our unique gifts to the well-being of the Planet.*

*This is a healing story.*

# Table of Contents

# Acknowledgments and Gratitude

We accomplish little alone.

The creation of this book involved many minds, hearts, and hands. The project has been a trial and a joy, and, like most things, unfolded at its own rate.

Numerous teachers have influenced my path, and to them I am deeply grateful. They include Angeles Arrien, whose teachings have helped me bridge insight with action; Jeanne Achterberg, Reb Anderson and Rusa Chiu, Michael Barenbaum, Jean Shinoda Bolen, Larry Brilliant, Lee Bycel, Ram Dass, Larry and Barbara Dossey, Lawrence Kushner, Manouso Manos, Robert and Ellen McDermott, Jacob Needleman, John O'Donohue, Patrick O'Neil, Rachel Naomi Remen, Bruce Spivey, Brian Swimme, Judyth Weaver, and Jon Kabat-Zinn.

Dr. G. Venkataswamy and his blessed family at the Aravind Eye Hospital in India serve as models of the power of compassionate service.

Derryck J. Dias and his staff provided encouragement and major support in manuscript preparation. Michael Mannion, Liv Williams-O'Keefe, Debra Goldstein, Gail Ross, and Jim Herwitz, provided early impetus. Joanne and Keith Harrison made it clear that my voice needed to be heard.

Many dear friends, associates, patients, and my colleagues at the Institute for Health & Healing at California Pacific Medical Center, Marin General Hospital, and Mills-Peninsula Health Services knowingly and unknowingly were major sources of input and inspiration. Cassie Stevens and Rennie Lindner were always patient with their administrative and moral support. Judith Tolson pushed me to tell my stories and not merely synthesize the viewpoints of others. Carol Spence brought my crude first draft to a workable manuscript form. Doris Mitsch then helped strengthen it with some artful pruning and shaping. Karen Cooper merged artwork and word and made the manuscript presentable. Sophie Kessler drew the Mobius strip image. Claudia Wood brought the project to the finish line with help from Janice Hoobler, Finola Poynton, and Doug Winger. Carl Hart crossed the t's and dotted the i's. Dave Razavi made the most of the author's photo.

The images for each step were created by Charles Hobson and originally appeared in *Human Touch: Images for a Garden.* The pen and ink images were engraved into granite stepping stones for a garden at the Palo Alto Medical Foundation in Palo Alto, California. Sandra Hobson collected the accompanying quotations dealing with the human spirit.

Doris Mitsch created the cover photograph. It is a study of a flower of the medicinally active *Datura* family. *Daturas* are widely used by medicine men and women of many cultures and are regarded as sacred. They are valued for their healing properties and their power to induce visionary dreams and reveal the causes of disease.

Most of all, I would like to thank my dear family. My wife, soul mate, and main pathfinder, Susy; my sons, Ben and Joe; my daughter-in-law Juliana; my grandson and teacher Eli; my granddaughters Sophia and Grace; as well as my parents, sister Melanie, and brother-in-law Eliot deserve special mention. Their love has taught me the meaning of prosperity and made my dreams come true.

# Foreword

*Deep Medicine* is an exceptional, visionary guide and pioneering resource for medicine of the future. If you accept the premise that we are all responsible for our own health and well-being, then it follows that we are all healers.

As Medical Director of the Institute for Health & Healing at the California Pacific Medical Center in San Francisco, Dr. William Stewart successfully practices and advocates a holistic approach to health and healing which is not only combined with contemporary medicine, but also suggests a worldview that includes everything as an ingredient contributing to our well-being. Stewart's most compelling message is that "Everything is either health creating or health negating, everything." To be responsible for our own well-being, we need to look at the daily choices we are making—are they health-creating or health-negating choices?

Cross-culturally, the power of choice for human beings contains three functions. Through choice, human beings are able to create new realities or conditions, to sustain current realities or conditions, and to let go of or end realities or conditions not desired or outgrown.

According to Dr. Stewart, everything we think, feel, say, and do is a choice contributing to either restoring health or negating health. Seeing health from this truly holistic perspective motivates us to make choices that serve our personal wellness, contribute to enduring public health, and aid planetary healing. This is the frontier of health and healing and the pivotal choice point for medicine of the future.

Dr. Stewart remains the singular and foremost way-shower of this transformative, evolutionary healing path—his vision provides "a middle way" that empowers responsible healthcare and health-creating choices. *Deep Medicine* reminds us that eradicating disease, creating health, and preventing future illness are personal and collective sacred tasks—just as the word health comes from the same root origin as the words whole and holy. Let us begin our sacred work and choose health for ourselves, others, and the world.

**Angeles Arrien, Ph.D.**
*Cross-Cultural Anthropologist*

# Introduction

## *Don't* Take Only As Directed

*Deep Medicine* is a book about the meaning of health and making health-creating change.

Every day we are inundated by images of health. Youthful images of men and women permeate our media, reinforcing popular ideas of health and beauty. Quick-fix workout programs and silver bullet pills and diets claim to help impatient consumers lose weight and live a healthier life. But most of these images and healing remedies are superficial and inadequate. Although science and medicine have advanced significantly in the past few decades, somewhere along the way our view of health has been blurred. Health is not about how beautiful you look, how old you are, or how big your muscles are. Health is about balance. Health is about survival. Health is about love. Health is about deep medicine.

Our own personal health depends on what we do and who we are. Health necessitates proper nutrition, appropriate physical activity, rest and relaxation, and the support of social networks. We are healthy when we are in a state of balance and equilibrium regarding our bodily processes and in relationship to our surroundings. When we lose this balance, we become ill. *Deep Medicine* engages health and well-being from the perspective that everything is either health creating or health negating. Everything that we think, feel, and do impacts our state of well-being.

*Deep Medicine* looks beneath the superficiality of symptoms to the underlying issues of health. It explores the complex, interwoven nature of health as part of the immense mystery of life rather than reducing health to an easily explainable puzzle, hastily solved. Our bodies should not be treated like machines that can be fixed by merely changing a part or using a standard healing process. Without deeper inquiry and self-discovery, short courses to well-being will likely fall short of promised results and will be unsustainable for most people. The work of health-creation and healing is a personal, lifelong, and conscious process that must examine the inner depths as well as refine surface contours.

Our work and growth toward vital well-being, optimal aging, and rapid, sustainable recovery from illness require committed introspection. True health necessitates reflection and physical exercise, quiet listening and determined action, food for thought as well as calorie counting, and support from caring loved ones as well as expert advice and treatment.

*Deep Medicine* connects our personal health with everything that surrounds us. It integrates simple remedies with lifelong learning and practice in an effort to create an optimal path to health. It is this integration that provides the greatest potential for meaningful, lasting, and truly transformative living. *Deep Medicine* is a book with perspectives and practices that are accessible and relevant. It is a book that will serve as a foundation for health-creating action, fostering self discovery, self efficacy, and self-directed healing long after the popular health fads of today have faded from memory.

## What Works for You

*We know what to do.* We are instructed and educated by multiple sources every day.

*We know how to do it.* A host of plans, programs, books, CDs, lectures, workshops, and retreats are available to us.

*But do we do it?* Not usually. It is much easier to buy the book than to read it, shop for the walking shoes than use them, or join the yoga class than attend it. It is noteworthy how many people will use an expensive pharmaceutical or undergo an invasive surgical procedure, rather than give up a sedentary lifestyle, change unhealthy eating habits, or forgo addictive behavior. What propels us to change and what prevents us from desired change? Change and changing are true challenges on the path to health and healing. What is really most important regarding our health generation is not the particular diet plan or exercise program we choose to pursue, but the actual *doing it!* The "doing" requires a deep, personal evocation of motivation, will, and action, and is much more difficult than "deciding." Dedication, discipline, and commitment are requirements. What you really need to know about health is not only how to start the specific tasks of a valuable program, but how to sustain the demanding work.

Most people know that they should take better care of themselves. And yet, somehow, a wide gap exists between knowing this and actually doing it. Quite often it takes a crisis: a frightening diagnosis, or symptoms we can't ignore. Then, when we realize our health problems have become advanced and serious, we turn to experts for guidance and care.

But even when under the care of an expert, lifestyle choices continue to have a tremendous impact on our state of well-being and our healing progress.

Wouldn't it be wonderful if we could begin to make health-creating choices and changes before the crisis comes? Learning to walk on the balance beam is easier when it is on the ground than when it is suspended six feet in the air. Establishing a solid foundation for health before a major crisis can help us cope and may even prevent a serious occurrence.

We cannot merely prescribe, order, or even wish health or healing any more than we can mandate happiness or demand creativity. What we can do is establish the cornerstones, plot the course, and gather the tools for healthy living. Ultimately, we each need to build and trust our own experience. We need to do our own insightful thinking, planning, and prioritizing, and make our own commitments to action. But we can't do it alone. Guides, maps, and commentary help to facilitate the steps, navigate the pitfalls and obstacles, find oases, and integrate the learnings.

This book proposes a self-generated action plan for your personal health objectives—one that makes the most of each person's unique capacity to respond, and acknowledges each individual's personal agenda, timeframe, strengths, and weaknesses. In a straightforward way, it presents the knowledge and skills that can help you make and sustain health-creating changes in your life.

The concepts in this book are evidence-based and grounded in the health-creating fundamentals of nutrition, physical activity, relaxation/ contemplation, and social connection. In exploring our health issues, we find ourselves dealing with the need for commitment, discipline, courage, honesty, responsibility, and accountability. These are *character issues* and they are fundamental to the development of optimal health.

## Why This Book—and Why Now?

Whether you are coping with a life-threatening illness, living with a chronic condition, or seeking general well-being, this book can serve you. *Deep Medicine* is a complement to popular books and fads promising instant health. Initiating and sustaining health-creating change is not a 10-step or 8-week short course, but a lifelong challenge. Short courses and quick-fix solutions can only be complements to a healthy lifestyle if they are associated with a strong foundation and deep understanding of health. *Deep Medicine* engages that reality in theory *and* practice by providing a basis on which all health decisions can be made.

## The Institute for Health & Healing

Early on in my medical career, I believed that living a healthy life was the responsibility of an individual, but healing was the responsibility of a doctor. Over the past 40 years, my views of health and healing have changed dramatically. I have been a surgeon for over 25 years. During this time, I have seen patients lose their sight, succumb to cancer, and recover miraculously. As I have grown as a surgeon and person, I have come to realize that healing is a deep and mysterious process, much more complex than anatomy and physiology can explain.

In the course of my quest to understand healing, I co-founded the Institute for Health & Healing at the California Pacific Medical Center in San Francisco. At its core, the Institute bridges eastern and western medicine, conventional and complementary practices, and the scientific and the sacred. At the Institute, classes, support groups, retreats, workshops, in-hospital and out-patient care, and basic and clinical research combine self-care and expert care in an ongoing collaboration. Over the years, many lives have been changed.

The Institute for Health & Healing exists to combine the best of conventional medicine with proven healing practices from around the world. Since its inception, we have carefully evaluated our encounters. Thousands of people have completed questionnaires assessing effectiveness, relevance, and results. Our clients' symptoms, attitudes, and progress toward goals have been recorded and reviewed. Our findings have led us to develop a fundamental and sustainable self-care program. At the heart of this program are the four pillars of self-care: (1) nutrition, (2) physical activity, (3) deep relaxation and contemplation, and (4) personal and community relationships.

The effectiveness of blending ancient and contemporary medicine is demonstrated by the more than 50,000 people the Institute for Health & Healing touches every year. In fact, after an extensive national survey, *Natural Health* magazine named California Pacific Medical Center "America's Healthiest Hospital," granting this honor largely because of the Institute for Health & Healing.

## How to Use this Book

This book provides an introduction to a lifelong journey toward health. It is very much a workbook. However, I won't tell you exactly what to do in these pages. Instead, you will be exposed to many ideas and asked what the next healing step is that will support health creation and authenticity in your life.

The chapters can be considered "steps." While there is no rigid, fixed, or formulaic recipe for change or healing, progress tends to occur in sequence, with each advance building on the previous one and setting the stage for the next. Each step provides exercises and questions to stimulate your exploration and help you identify your personal issues, guideposts, and directional choices.

There are no right or wrong answers. The questions are meant to encourage your self-inquiry and discovery. Some might prefer a set of clearly defined recommended actions over a specific period of time. It is challenging to honestly answer open-ended questions and fill in the blanks for yourself, rather than have someone else do it for you. It is also empowering. You are the one who must select the most relevant questions to ask yourself and determine what to do about important insights you unearth. You are the one who will determine the right medicine at the right time and how best to take it. Don't think that you need to answer all of the questions at the same time. Take a small step. Address a specific area of interest. Look for one or two approaches that speak to you about lending balance to your life, and try them. Build patiently from there.

Throughout the book, I cite real-life examples and stories from my own journey. Some examples will be based on scientific data and proven facts of the human condition. Others will be intuitive, imaginative, or guided by practical experience. By these examples, insight and experience are gained, lessening the distance between knowing what you need to do and doing it.

*Deep Medicine* is a philosophy and an application of that philosophy. As such it is a handbook to better health—not a rule book or instruction manual. It will help connect the dots between the multiple factors that influence your health.

*Deep Medicine* will help you move toward health and healing in a deliberate, constructive way. You will experience a dynamic construct that builds upon itself through successes, learnings, and course corrections.

After reading *Deep Medicine*, you will have an evolving, transformative, and personal plan for health that will last a lifetime.

## Step One

# What Is Health?
# What Is Healing?

TO EVERY THING
THERE IS A SEASON,
AND A TIME TO EVERY PURPOSE
UNDER HEAVEN.

*ECCLESIASTES 3:1*

*Healing has always been the common meeting ground between the physical and the spiritual. When we experience illness, even something as minor as a cold or the flu, we are brought face to face with our vulnerability, and if we look ahead, which we are prone to do at such moments, we can see death. As a result, illness has always been a breeding ground for spiritual concerns.*

**– Larry Dossey, M.D.**
Reinventing Medicine

*The body is your temple.*
*Keep it pure and clean for the soul to reside in.*

**– B.K.S. Iyengar**

One of my earliest childhood memories is playing doctor as a preschooler, with a toy stethoscope and a clinic of ailing stuffed animals. Not too many years later, this game became reality as I began my medical training.

In the 1960s, while I was in college and medical school, dramatic change was in the air in medicine. Heart surgeons were performing magic at the body's core. Organ transplantation was the new focus for pioneers and visionaries. Imaging equipment that would revolutionize diagnostic capabilities was on the drawing board. New drugs, based on exploding research efforts, were flooding the marketplace, and government-sponsored health insurance for the elderly—Medicare—was initiated, sparking the fear of socialized medicine in the hearts of established practitioners.

During my years in practice, I have witnessed many trends and repercussions in medicine. I have seen biotechnical wizardry fulfill the public's demand for state-of-the-art medical developments at the nearest hospital—a trend that has collided with financial constraints and resource rationing. I have seen an increasingly informed and sophisticated public demand a more caring, compassionate application of medicine. I have seen surgery and miracle drugs save lives, specialists displace generalists and back again, requests for every possible life support device, and requests for no treatment at all—only a wish to be at home surrounded by loved ones. I have seen private hospitals go bankrupt, teaching institutions merge for survival, public hospitals fail to handle the workload of uninsured patients, and for-profit hospital conglomerates list themselves on the New York Stock Exchange.

My practice began in general surgery training and evolved into one of highly specialized ophthalmic plastic and reconstructive surgery. I have since become medical director of an institute integrating holistic and conventional practices with an increasing emphasis on education, leadership, and service. I have operated barefoot in India with hand-held flashlights. I've encountered acupuncturists in pain clinics, massage therapists in intensive care units, and chaplains on hospital rounds. I have seen unexplained recoveries from terminal illness, and I have seen people die for no apparent reason. I have come to appreciate how tortuous the path and how complex the contributing factors are to each person's illness and well-being. I have learned that there is no single, simple path to health.

## Our Understanding of Health Is Changing

The boundaries of health practice are changing, and the legacy of healing practice is rich. The mapping of the human genome is occurring at the same time that traditional Chinese medicine and Ayurvedic medicine (from India) are becoming better known in Western cultures. All herald an approach to medical care tailored to each person, rather than a generalized, statistical approach to disease. There is an individual and collective movement toward balance, collaboration, integration, and wholeness demonstrated by the growing popularity of complementary and alternative medicine. The times are fertile with opportunity for understanding health and healing in their broadest, deepest implications.

Amazing developments have occurred in healthcare in recent years and in the previous century. We are the beneficiaries of an expanding realm of knowledge, with practices from many traditions and cultures. We can never underestimate the power, value, and primacy of modern medicine.

Yet, despite these medical advances, people are increasingly burned out, stressed out, and overwhelmed, while the incidence of chronic illness is rising for all age groups. We have too much work and not enough time for ourselves. We lament our schedules and then burden them further. We eat too much, drink too much, sleep too little, and don't get enough exercise. We manifest the physical, mental, and emotional signs and symptoms of a host of maladies. Our stomachs make too much acid, our hearts constrict in pain, our breathing is labored. Our joints and muscles swell and stiffen, our skin itches and erupts. We succeed, but we are left unfulfilled. What can we learn from these phenomena?

There's no shortage of healthcare professionals to consult or dearth of books, lectures, workshops, or practices to pencil into our schedules. Even these may be another source of stress. If we already have too much to do, adding more heightens our anxiety.

Again and again we have choices between conflicting possibilities: do we go to work to make money to pay the mortgage, school tuition, and save for retirement—or do we take time off to be with family and enjoy a holiday? Do we eat broccoli or a bacon cheeseburger? Shall we watch television or go outside and get some exercise? Can we deny ourselves the instant gratification for some potential future benefit? Can we learn from our pain and suffering?

Often we know the consequences, but choose unwisely anyway. Why? Are we ambivalent about our health? "It won't happen to me," or "I'll make up for it tomorrow," we tell ourselves—until a crisis strikes. The heart attack, the cancer diagnosis, a death in the family, or a failed job or relationship changes everything. Too often, a crisis is the "wake-up call" that first tells us how far our lives have swung out of balance.

## Health Is Balance—Healing Is Change

I was once asked in an invigorating discussion with bright young students to define health in one word. After a brief, thoughtful silence I said, "Balance." A follow up question quickly surfaced. "If health is balance, then what is healing?" My response was instantaneous—"Change."

The word health comes from the Indo-European word, *kailo*. This root word is the origin of the English words whole and holy, as well as health. While today our concept of health is typically limited to our physical and mental status, the legacy of the word itself implies something broader—and well it should.

If our understanding of health is limited to its physical and mental aspects, we risk being blind to its spiritual, social, and mythological influences. To understand the true nature of our health, we must try to understand these parts as well as their cumulative whole.

Dialogue about health often uses terms like alternative, complementary, mind-body, and mainstream medicine. This tendency to categorize is limiting. Such a reductionist vocabulary might block the perspective that can help us to integrate these categories.

But integration does not mean homogenization. Our medical practice should not be one nondescript blend, but should honor our many facets. If we were discussing integration with regard to food, we would never suggest mixing Italian, French, Chinese, and Mexican food together into some international ecumenical goulash. We prefer to savor the distinctive, valued aspects of each depending on the time and context. Do we feel like hot and spicy, or subtle and soothing? The same meal at every mealtime would not be particularly healthy or satisfying.

Our perspective needs to intertwine all the parts into the complex pattern that makes up health. It is a setting not of either/or relationships, but of both/and relationships, emphasizing collaboration rather than competition. Health is a major domain of our lives. It cannot be separated easily from other major domains such as: work/creative purpose; relationship (to self, intimate other, groups, collectives, nature, the Divine, mystery, spirit); and our sense of prosperity, resources, abundance, and blessing.

Healing is a process of change—the journey to the balance and wholeness of health. Growth, aging, sickness, recovery, and death are also processes of change. Being healthy means more than attaining an ideal weight, producing "normal" lab test results, or conforming to the legal definition of sanity. Healing also is forgiveness, confession, reconciliation, and rectification. Health does not mean being completely free of illness. It does not mean defying death indefinitely.

Being healthy means a wholeness in the living of one's life—a dynamic and constantly changing balance that acknowledges the soundness of our physical state, the wholesomeness of lifestyle, the values that define our behavior, our intimate and collective relationships, the meaning and purpose of our work in the world, and the spiritual dimension of our existence. It is about human values as well as lab values. It requires attention to our inner domains as well as our outer world. It is not a static destination where we will at some point arrive and then reside indefinitely. Daily, hourly, even momentary variations, adjustments, and course corrections are the norm. How we "feel" in the morning is likely to have changed by noon.

The challenges to our health are internal and external, individual and collective. They include genetic, environmental, communal, cultural, physical, mental, and spiritual factors. These factors are so varied, numerous, and interwoven that discerning cause and effect can be difficult.

Attempting to be holistic does not eliminate the need to examine the relevant parts. Yet, as with determining causative factors, no combination of words can capture the full effect of mind-body-spirit wholeness. Health may be seen as the manifestation of everything we think, feel, say, do, and are. *Ultimately, everything is either health creating or health negating. Everything!*

## There's A Bigger Picture

Today's dominant medical model defines our diseases and illnesses in primarily physical and epidemiologic terms: bacterial meningitis (infection of brain linings), gastric ulcer (erosion of stomach lining), osteoporosis (loss of density of bone), myocardial infarction (death of the heart muscle), and so on. These terms, while useful, don't express how varied factors contribute to any given state of illness or wellness. They can be misleading, when people take them to mean that every illness has a single, specific cause. We also tend to look at disease in a species-specific and population-based way. Incidences and prevalences of diseases are calculated for various populations. Responses to treatments are reported as percents of those who responded to a particular drug intervention.

Our very existence is characterized in mainly physical or material terms. We are labeled as a student, teacher, mother, plumber, salesperson, and so forth. These names are woefully inadequate to capture the full grandeur of our human condition: our roots, our potential, and the vast interplay in which we find ourselves. We are not only human doings, but we are human beings. We are not just our jobs, accomplishments, roles, activity lists, or group memberships. Nor are we just our thoughts, emotions, or mistakes.

To ignore the nonphysical aspects of our existence (e.g., spirit, soul, conscience, intuition) is to have an incomplete picture.

Seeing ourselves from a physical and nonphysical viewpoint is not just a trend in New Age thinking or alternative healthcare. The World Health Organization has defined health as not simply an absence of disease, but as a positive state of physical, mental, and social well-being. In 1984, the World Health Assembly added "spiritual health" to its definition of health. More recently, a wealth of solid, scientific evidence is coming forth supporting the effects of such influences as prayer, intention, and social support on our state of well-being (see the Readings and References appendix).

It is the harmonizing of many different factors that leads us to health. This requires relating many aspects of our lives. Our work toward health and healing, as the origin of the words implies, is not just physical work, but sacred work toward wholeness. This comprehensive perspective is an essential element of sustainable individual and communal health. In times of collective fear and despair, the pursuit of health is "soul work." This deep, inner work must accompany our physical and material concerns in order for real healing to occur.

## Holistic Treatment of Illness

Biotechnical (Western) medicine is primarily concerned with diagnosing and treating disease— that is, seeking a cure. A disease is considered an abnormality in the structure and function of bodily organs and systems, and a cure is sought to correct that abnormality.

The experience of illness includes all the difficulties that a disease creates—dependency, fear, isolation, inability to make a living, and limitations in the activities of daily life such as eating, moving about, and personal hygiene. Illness might even be defined as the experience of being devalued personally and socially during a sickness. Illness, and its attendant suffering, can even occur in the absence of a measurable disease.

It's been estimated that at least 40 and as many as 75 percent of visits to the doctor are for complaints without an ascertainable pathologic basis. What's more, an estimated 80 percent of all episodes of being "sick" are managed outside the formal healthcare system—meaning that people are taking care of themselves as best they can, often without seeing a doctor.

While doctors may be primarily interested in the recognition and treatment of disease, patients are mainly concerned with the difficulties and discomfort that their sickness imparts—their illness. Each view is incomplete, but both are absolutely necessary for accessing the richly complex and multi-layered arenas of health and healing.

In their 1978 article, "Culture, Illness, and Care: Clinical Lessons from Anthropologic and Cross-Cultural Research," in the *Annals of Internal Medicine*, Dr. Arthur Kleinman and his associates report a small but instructive study and make some very relevant recommendations on distinguishing between disease and illness.

Dr. Kleinman conducted a study in Taiwan using one hundred patients who went to see indigenous healers. The vast majority of patients were found to be suffering from disorders that fell into one of three main groups: minimal, self-limited diseases that run their course and resolve; non-life-threatening chronic diseases in which related psychological and social problems were the chief concerns; and somatization—in which physical complaints represented mental illness. (Mind and body are not separated in the Chinese medical construct, and mental illness has been culturally stigmatized.)

Kleinman and his colleagues also followed up a subgroup of patients to assess the efficacy of the treatment received. Ten out of twelve reported their treatment as successful—some even when their physical symptoms didn't improve. The two patients who reported their treatment as unsuccessful were the only patients with severe medical or psychiatric disease (acute kidney infection and acute depressive syndrome). The researchers interpreted their findings to mean that *illness* predominates for most patients visiting indigenous healers. Treatment was considered successful when it impacted the patients' *illness*. The patients with documented pathologic *diseases* were not successfully treated by the indigenous healers.

To get at the distinction between disease and illness and serve the large number of people seeking healing—not just a cure for a condition—Kleinman has suggested using the following open-ended questions as part of the doctor-patient conversation. You can also use them for your own personal assessment of the conditions and situations for which you do and don't seek professional healthcare:

1.  What do you call your problem?
2.  What do you think caused your problem?
3.  Why do you think it started when it did?
4.  What do you think your sickness does to you?
5.  How severe is your sickness? Will it have a long or a short course?
6.  What kind of treatment do you think you should receive and what are the most important results you hope to receive from this treatment?
7.  What are the main problems your sickness has caused for you?
8.  What do you fear most about your sickness?

Considering these questions and the data suggesting that the vast majority of sicknesses are subject only to self-care, we can see the vital role each one of us can play in our own health and healing. This is especially significant since our diseases and illnesses are often associated with life events.

### "Life Moment"

When I returned to San Francisco after the death of my father in Arizona, I hit a post with my car in the hospital parking lot, threw out my back stepping distractedly off a curb, and came down with a serious upper-respiratory infection. Even without accurately knowing specific cause-and-effect relationships—e.g., increased susceptibility to infection because of immune system suppression from "stress"—my health-related responses are a compelling illustration of the associations between our life's circumstances and our state of well-being.

I am sure that every reader has similar stories of when illness struck during periods of challenge. For example, it has been reported that the most common time for heart attacks to occur in men is Monday morning, and that students are most likely to become ill during final exams.

## Our Path to Health and Healing

Jeanne Achterberg, in her book *Woman as Healer*, defines healing as follows:

- Healing is a lifelong journey toward wholeness.
- Healing is remembering what has been forgotten about connection and unity and interdependence among all things living and non-living.
- Healing is embracing what is most feared.
- Healing is opening what has been closed, softening what has been hardened into obstruction.
- Healing is entering into the transcendent, timeless moment when one experiences the Divine.
- Healing is creativity and passion and love.
- Healing is seeking and expressing self in its fullness, its light and shadow, its male and female.
- Healing is learning to trust life.

Philosopher and writer Wayne Muller has also suggested expanding the medical model of inquiry. Usually medical inquiry is focused on the present and past medical illness. Muller suggests that history taking should expand to the full story of any patient. When we make a diagnosis, we are actually naming a condition. Does our naming set the full context for the condition? Having named the condition, we need a treatment plan that is also an action plan expansive enough to engage as many aspects of the disease and the illness as possible.

The medical diagnosis of heart disease, resulting in chest pain due to narrowed arteries supplying blood to the heart, does not indicate in what other ways a person's heart may be broken, closed, weak, or less than whole. What can we learn from our symptoms and diagnoses? How can we capture factors such as social isolation, anger, and hostility—all known cardiac risk factors—in our naming of a disease or illness?

These definitions move us beyond the medicine of symptoms—be they mental or physical—toward core issues such as fear, dependence, creativity, passion, trust, awe, and love. In fact, love is often described as the strongest healing force on the planet. Love has many limbs and takes many forms. Acknowledgment, forgiveness, and respect are limbs of love. The love of parent, child, spouse, and friend, and of beauty, nature, and the Divine are all forms of love. How we engage these features of ourselves that are deeper than our personality traits (bright, elegant, fun, sober, efficient) and represent our character (committed, courageous, honest, loyal, trustworthy) will be reflected in the nature of our health and healing. Working with our character issues is part of deep medicine.

## The Character of Health

When health is discussed and possibilities for improvement or change are raised, the topic often involves a new diet, exercise program, vitamin, or supplement. These options seem attractive since they are usually simple, short-term, and highly touted by their various advocates. We are all seduced by the possibility of a short, sweet solution to our dilemma or need. We like the quick, easy fix.

There is nothing wrong with wanting the solution to our challenges to be quick and easy—except that in real life, it just doesn't often occur.

In exploring health issues, we inevitably find ourselves dealing with such necessities as penetrating self-inquiry; rigorous honesty with ourselves about our strengths, weaknesses, resources, obstacles, and circumstances; the need for commitment and discipline to sustain our program over time; the deep sense of responsibility we must carry toward our objectives; and the courage and humility we must display to seek help where and when we need it and to stay the course.

These are character issues—matters that our parents, grandparents, teachers, mentors and coaches have presented to us many times. The choice of program or modality becomes less important than the authentic engagement of character development on our path to well-being. I am talking about philosophy, not fads. I am proposing a process of lifelong learning and commitment done at your pace, not as a time-limited short course. I am referring to deep, internal transformation, not a surface remodel. This is foundation work—not a fresh coat of paint. This is the challenge of change.

The questions are deeper than "carbohydrates or proteins?" The choices are not limited to which class—yoga or T'ai Chi or meditation or spin?—but demand an in-depth appreciation of who we are, where we have come from, and where we are going at the most fundamental, intimate, personal level. No one teacher, no one way can provide the answers. Each of us must create the answers for ourselves, and it requires the development of true character to succeed.

## The Time Is Now

Building character demands our rapt attention to the present moment. We must be alert not to wallow in past disappointments or wounds. We cannot waste our precious energy worrying or fantasizing about what might or might not happen. If we dissipate our life force on the past or the future, we will not have the personal resources to fully engage the present. We must learn from the past, yet it is in the present where we reside. It is in the present where we choose to heal the past and create the future. We remember the lessons and learning of the past without being ensnared or stuck there. We plan and prepare carefully for the future without investing completely in what might or might not come to pass.

Our energy belongs in the present. Herein lives the wisdom of sages from many perspectives who teach us to be awake, mindful, ready, and in the now. The essence of our growth in life is to be present and to build our character. If we can do these two things, our contentment and well-being will follow.

## It Is in Our Hands

Part of the true pursuit of health requires self-responsibility. We can be guided by the advice of experts, but also need to accept personal responsibility for our health. Finding our personal path to health requires our appreciation of the complex, multi-dimensional existence in which we find ourselves. It also requires our identifying what is really important to us and building the confidence to act on these things.

However, there is a difference between accepting responsibility for moving forward with health-creating, healing choices and taking blame for what does not seem to be working. If your condition is not cured, it does not mean that you didn't meditate, visualize, or visit the oncologist enough. Taking responsibility for playing an active role in your own health and healing is not the same as blaming or judging failed modalities or yourself in relation to them. The important thing is to invest fully in what you're doing. Give it your "best shot" and then be open to the outcome.

Take the initiative to get the necessary information to make informed choices and give informed consent. Take the responsibility to act on the information, knowledge, and advice you gather.

By working in collaboration with your caregivers, you become a primary care provider to yourself.

When you have a clearer view of the many factors affecting health, you'll know that even an ominous diagnosis is just one piece of the big picture. Health just isn't as precise as a medical diagnosis. The meaning of any medical diagnosis must be considered in relation to many influencing factors. Understanding overarching relationships is part of gaining a perspective that can help lead us all to healthful living, even when faced with serious illness.

For example, such subjective variables as our will to live and the nature and the extent of our support networks have a tremendous effect on our health. Miracle cures and spontaneous remissions occur and sometimes the right drug or the best surgery is unsuccessful.

## Quick Fix or Lasting Solution?

Regardless of any diagnosis you may carry or any
name or definition of yourself with which you
identify, you can be aware of the implications and
importance of your role. You can mobilize yourself
to do something about it.

An exercise program, a stress reduction course,
a new diet, the latest supplement or vitamin extract,
a workshop, the newest book, or a promise of health
may draw you...but let the buyer beware! The lost
weight is gained back about 90 percent of the time;
the "Ten Easy Steps" are either too easy and nothing
happens or too hard and aren't done; instant
enlightenment isn't that fast; and fifteen minutes
per day isn't quite enough for total fitness. It is fairly
safe to say that the quick fix, or easy solution—as
alluring as it might sound—is just plain illusory.
Compliance with any medical or health program is
difficult to maintain.

The path to healing is long, strewn with
obstacles, and without end. Health is a moving
target and the journey is not to it, but about it. It is
about standing, lying, walking, running, dancing,
eating, fighting, soaring, diving, wishing, praying,
thinking, feeling, learning, and choosing. Deep
medicine is about attitude and action and the
capacity to stick to the chosen course.

In addition, our healing in some circumstances
may actually involve accepting the reality of the
incurable nature of whatever condition might be
afflicting us. After all, in the end we are all "terminal
cases."

From our physical frailty and limitations to the limitless expanse of our inner, spiritual landscape, understanding health requires several basic reminders:

- The essence of health is holistic: even as we acknowledge and accept the physical aspects of health and disease, health creation and healing need to be recognized as nonmaterial aspects of life as well.
- The driving forces in our collective healthcare and wellness today are material: economic, political, and scientific.
- The basic building block of health and healing is relationship: to self, to intimate others, to community, to the planet, and to the sacred or spiritual aspect of life.
- Personal transformation—a deep philosophic shift—is often necessary if life choices are to be lasting and sustainable.
- The core challenge is, "How do I go about changing?"

The time to start the healing road is now—don't wait for a crisis to jolt your awareness. The trip can even be fun.

You will be required to chart your own course and create your own action/business plan. You will be the driver, the vehicle, and the timekeeper. It is not a practice run—this is it!

In the words of Martin Luther:

*This life, therefore,*
*is not perfection*
*but growth in perfection,*
*not health but healing,*
*not being but becoming,*
*not rest but exercise.*
*We are not what*
*we shall be*
*but we are growing*
*toward it,*
*the process is not*
*yet finished*
*but it is going on,*
*this is not the end*
*but it is the road.*

⌘ **Exercise for Step One:** ⌘
**Choosing to Begin**

Looking at your state of health and assessing it, as your favorite healthcare practitioner might, is a powerful exercise. Use the following outline to define your present condition and begin developing a diagnosis (naming) and a treatment (action) plan.

## Personal Health Assessment Questionnaire

These questions, grouped in five general areas, should bring you in touch with many lifestyle issues. While our inherited genetics and the intangibles of luck, fate, and destiny play a large part in health, lifestyle is also a critical determinant of well-being—and we can actually do something about that as we play the hand we are dealt!

### 1. Overview

What breakthrough/change would you most like to achieve with regard to health? How important is this change to you? How confident are you that you can achieve this change? Use a scale of your choosing, (e.g., **-10 → +10** *or* **1 → 10**) to record the present level of: 1) *importance*; and 2) *confidence* that you can do something about it. Consider your rankings and what is placing them at the levels you chose. Why not higher or lower?

- What are your current and previous medical problems?
- Specifically, what symptoms are you experiencing?
- Are there recurring themes—physical, mental, emotional, and/or spiritual?

- Can you identify areas of weakness? Areas of strength?
- What medications, vitamins, or natural remedies (e.g., herbs) are you currently using?
- Do you know why you are using them?
- Are they helping?
- Are you aware of their effects—both good and bad? Have you monitored these effects with a *symptom journal?*
- What significant illnesses run in your family?
- Are there any recurrent themes?
- Are you like your parents? Do you see your parents in your own illnesses?
- Review your family of origin—your parents and siblings. Note aspects that relate to your present health status.

## 2. Life Habits

What does your diet say about you? Examine your diet for a typical week, including number of meals per day and how often you eat meat, dairy products, fish, vegetables, whole grains, and sweets.

- What are your addictions (tobacco, caffeine, alcohol, etc.) and why do you think you have chosen them?
- What foods do you crave? When do you crave them? Why?
- How do you respond to your craving?
- What is you current physical activity or exercise?
- What keeps you from exercising or engaging in physical activity?
- What encourages you to exercise or engage in physical activity?

## 3. Work/Social History

- What have been the most significant events in your life? How do you think they've impacted your health—both past and present?
- What is your marital or living status? Are you satisfied with it?
- Do you have social support networks to help you in times of distress? To share joyful times?
- What is your current job? Are you satisfied with it?
- How does your job impact your health? Would changing your job benefit your health?
- Describe the relationship between work, play, and rest for you. Is it a satisfactory ratio?
- Where are you currently living? Are you satisfied with your environment?

## 4. Body Image/Sexuality

- Does your self-image encourage or discourage healthy behavior?
- Are there issues in your sexuality that affect your well-being?

## 5. Guiding Values

- What values or principles guide you?
- Do you have sayings you live by? (e.g., keep a stiff upper lip; big boys don't cry; be a good girl)
- How would you describe your spirituality?
- Do you pray? For yourself? For others?
- Do you think your relationship with a higher power has anything to do with the quality of your life and health?

- What is your understanding of the greater good"?
- What is your "purpose"?
- What gives "meaning" to your life?

Having reviewed these various aspects of your life, how satisfied are you with the state of your health? Given this assessment, can you identify insights and learnings about yourself that will impact your health plan? Can you identify and prioritize changes that would serve your heath?

It may also be valuable to review your answers to these questions with your primary healthcare providers. (These questions are adapted from an assessment tool owned by The Institute for Health & Healing at California Pacific Medical Center, San Francisco, California, and used with permission.)

## Fast Track Self-Assessment

If the comprehensive health assessment above appears too long, too complicated, or too time consuming, try this **fast track self-assessment** by answering these three key questions:
- What am I thinking?
- What am I feeling?
- What am I doing about it?

These three questions can be used any time, any place, and about any subject to locate yourself and determine your next small right step in the process of health creation and risk reduction.

## Step Two

# Beginning the Shift:
# The Challenge of Change

ONE MAY NOT
REACH THE DAWN
SAVE BY THE PATH
OF THE NIGHT.

*KAHLIL GIBRAN*

*By a single thought that comes into mind,*
*in one moment, a hundred worlds are overturned.*

**– Rumi**

*We can rise above our limitations,*
*only once we recognize them.*

**– B.K.S. Iyengar**
Yoga: The Path to Holistic Health

A well-known Zen master visits New York City. Experiencing all the city has to offer, he goes up to a hot dog vendor and says, "Make me one with everything."

The hot dog vendor fixes a hot dog and hands it to the Zen master, who pays with a twenty dollar bill. The vendor puts the bill in the cash box and closes it. After a few moments of waiting patiently, "Where's my change?" asks the Zen master.

The vendor responds, "Change must come from within."

## What Is Shift?

Alone in his hospital room, severely ill with complications of alcoholism, William W. was filled with despair. His body ravaged, he realized that what he had been, he could no longer be. He said later, as noted in M.B. Liester's article, "Lying there in conflict, I dropped into black depression. Momentarily, my prideful obstinacy was crushed. I cried out, 'Now I am ready to do anything!'"

His world overturned, William W. went on to recover and found Alcoholics Anonymous, helping others to make the shift he made.

What does it take to get us to change our ways? Do we have to hit bottom like William W. to change? What moves us to carry on—or to throw in the towel? How much is enough? Where do we go from here? These questions lack precise answers—they are questions that stir the gut, touch the heart, and challenge the mind. These questions are relevant as we reflect upon the nature of being human. These are questions that raise issues that impact our health. We confront these issues on a regular basis, or we see them peeking around the corner at us.

After a shift, perception of the world is changed. The landscape is seen as never before. Biological change may drive the transformation as the caterpillar becomes the butterfly or as the snake sheds a skin that no longer fits. We understand what Marcel Proust must have meant when he said, "The real voyage of discovery consists not in seeking new landscapes but in having new eyes."

A classic shift occurs in the Dickens classic, *A Christmas Carol*, as Ebenezer Scrooge, visited by his ghosts, suddenly is able to see things from a totally different perspective and is radically transformed. Why was Scrooge moved to change? He was forced to recognize recurrent patterns in his life that were cruel—patterns that bound rather than protected him.

Each of us has recurrent patterns of behavior, habitual responses that repetitively lead us to dead-end relationships, frustrating work settings, chronic unhappiness, or illness. We get stuck in these responses. Changing our behavioral patterns is often more like major surgery than a quick adjustment. It requires insight, courage, and work. Only deep, elemental, internal change sustains meaningful, lasting external growth and progress. Even in a collective context, lasting social change requires personal transformation.

## The Challenge of Change

Change and our potential to change is a spectrum.
Several different stages of change are recognized:

1. *Pre-contemplation equilibrium:* We are not interested in changing.

2. *Contemplation/disorientation:* We begin to get the first inklings that a change might be in order.

3. *Preparation/exploration:* We begin to think about, talk about and research the options, possibilities.

4. *Action/reorientation:* We begin to take the steps to do what we need to do to change our ways.

5. *New equilibrium/maintenance:* We continue to practice what we have learned and create a new homeostasis, or balance, for ourselves.

Getting ready to change requires much more than having your faults pointed out or appreciating a need or desire or fear you carry that has opened you to the possibility of change. We first must be "motivated" to change. This means we must appreciate the importance of making a change and have a reasonable level of confidence that we can succeed. If importance and confidence are lacking, our chances of successfully changing are small. Miller and Rollnick in their superb book *Motivational Interviewing* emphasize the importance of motivation being *evoked* rather than *prescribed*. Physicians are taught to diagnose an illness and prescribe treatment.

Compliance to prescribed treatment regimens, however, is often dismal, only about one-quarter to one-third of people take medicines as prescribed, comply with treatment instructions, stick to diets, etc. Even when we do succeed initially, we often slip back (regain our lost weight or discontinue the exercise program) as the inspiration for beginning something is diluted by the hard work and perspiration that are required to sustain our desired change. That is why, as we shall see, our preparation and planning need to be realistic, and our initial steps need to be small enough and few enough in number to allow us early success. We need to fortify ourselves for the long haul, not the quick fix. Our motivation to do something—to change—must be our own (evoked), must come from within, and not be imposed upon us or prescribed from outside/external sources.

Miller and Rollnick describe "change talk" as one of the simplest and best parameters to observe in ascertaining someone's readiness to change. If suggestions for change are met with resistance talk—"That's a good idea, but..."; "I know that, however..."; "I've tried that and it didn't help"—it's a strong indicator that the time to act to change something may not be at hand. In these circumstances more preparation work is necessary to evoke the internal and personal desire and motivation to change. When, on the other hand change talk is present or elicited, it is a good sign that the time for change is present: "Yes, I'm ready at last..."; "I can't take it anymore..."; "It's time to do something about this and stop just talking/thinking about it." These differences seem obvious and simplistic. Nonetheless they are some of the best predictors to be attentive to as the possibility of health-creating change is considered for others *and* yourself!

If we are in a state of awareness and readiness, change will be much easier than if we are unmotivated to effect a change. Our ingrained habitual behaviors are difficult and challenging to change, but it is possible. Sustainable change can begin in a time frame as short as three to eight weeks. Changing our circumstances can be a useful way to start. If you don't bring home any ice cream from the store, it will be easier not to eat it when you get a craving. If you can break your behavior patterns into small enough fragments, the decisions of what to do may become easier. Rather than planning the major workout you are going to perform, and never getting out of the chair because the task seems too big, just decide to get up when the thought first hits you that you need some exercise. Then get yourself into your workout clothes, then out the door—even if you have not decided exactly what form of exercise you will do or where you will go.

In this way, you will be reinforcing your potential to do what needs doing. We have to start where we are, and small steps are okay!

I never learned to stand on my head as a child. I had often been challenged in my youth to stand on my own two feet, or to sit or stand up straight like a big boy, or a man. But unlike most children, I had never ventured onto my head upside down. I'll never forget the day as a grown man fifty years old that I first succeeded in balancing myself upside down. It was a goal I was determined to achieve.

It took years of meditation for the mental equanimity and years of T'ai Chi for the fluidity and readiness for a serious yoga practice. Then months of practice, instruction, guidance, coaching, and support to first get me comfortably, solidly upside down—beyond the fear and uncertainty. What I discovered was a new perspective, a new confidence and an enhanced sense of self-respect. For a mature man, steeped in science, trusting of expertise, impressed with excellence and success, I experienced my own balance and strength even when completely turned over. Now as I stand on my head (or my hands) for longer periods of time, I am growing in balance, alignment and ease. I feel a sense of accomplishment and it is fun! I am resonating in a posture that has a wisdom of its own and gives me a whole new lens with which to view the world.

## Seeing the Light

When we change our viewpoint or perspective, we see things differently. New possibilities arise. A liberation or breakthrough may occur. "Aha!" or "Eureka!" we may exclaim. A shift expands us beyond our usual ways of thinking, feeling, acting, and, in and of itself, is a giant step toward healing.

Sometimes a shift is necessary to get beyond obvious issues to underlying needs and patterns of behavior that require changing. Before they can be changed, they must be seen and admitted.

This seeing can require a host of visual dimensions: perspective, outlook, world view, perception, and insight. A shift is akin to wearing a new pair of glasses—glasses that clear our blurred vision (reading glasses) or that allow us to see a generally invisible part of the electromagnetic spectrum (infrared glasses).

Individuals who have reported sudden change were the subject of a study conducted by psychologists W.R. Miller and J.C. deBaca. They studied volunteer subjects who reported having been "transformed and noting ... a deep shift in core values, feelings, attitudes or actions." Their work was made known to me by psychiatrist, and Institute for Health & Healing colleague, Elisabeth Targ, M.D.

They reported the top four value priorities reported by men and women before and after their sudden change, or shift experience, were:

|  | Values Before Sudden Change | Values After Sudden Change |
| --- | --- | --- |
| **Men** | Wealth | Spirituality |
|  | Adventure | Personal Peace |
|  | Achievement | Family |
|  | Pleasure | God's Will |
| **Women** | Family | Growth |
|  | Independence | Self-Esteem |
|  | Career | Spirituality |
|  | Fitting In | Happiness |

Meaningful subjective experiences that prompt shifts in our values are common to us all. These experiences may take the form of rapture, awe, amazement, or peace—sensing a unity and natural relatedness to all around us. They may occur out of the blue or be preceded by a joyous event, a glorious sunset, illness, or despair.

## When Will Shift Occur?

The desire to shift or change may occur in each of us when the discomfort, pain, or "dis-ease" of staying the same becomes greater than the resistance and fear of changing. The particular circumstance that might initiate a cascade of change may be related to an unfulfilling job, a relationship lacking commitment and intimacy, an unhealed childhood wound, serious illness, the aging process, or even a near-death experience.

That which cries out for healing in each person is as unique as that individual's genetic makeup, history, and present circumstances. Although probing our backgrounds will be an important aspect of problem solving, getting stuck in revisiting the depths of past trauma may prevent one from dealing in today's reality. It is important that our true reality is in the present. Balancing learnings from past events with future possibilities, we engage the dynamic tension of the present.

We cannot create a shift until we have the *tools*. In addition to personal inspiration, commitment and desire for change, the tools for a shift must include a *knowledge* base and a philosophic *perspective* that will provide the strategies that make our change meaningful and sustainable. We also need *skills*—techniques and tactics that lead us through transition toward self-knowledge and help us translate our discoveries into practical action.

Seeing things in a new way or adopting a new philosophy is not about joining a sect or cult, nor about giving up religious or scientific beliefs. It is about connecting to internal wisdom, trusting the inner voice and responding to its messages. It requires the courage of being who you really are. e.e.cummings wrote that "it takes great courage to grow up to be who you really are."

Courage is required because sometimes that which is our personal truth may be in opposition to a peer group or against accepted convention. Courage does not imply being free of fear or uncertainty. Rather it is acting constructively in the presence of fear. Meaningful change, contrary to popular belief, will require our leaving our comfort zone. We profess to welcome the possibility of a change as long as we can stay in our comfort zone or the setting is deemed safe. But the very nature of real change demands that we often break behavior patterns or habits that—while they may be detrimental to our health and well-being—feel safe, are known, and provide us a sense of stability. Stable patterns are necessary lest we live in chaos, so it is difficult for us to leave our patterns of behavior even when they are no longer useful, constructive or health creating. Being ourselves may mean standing up for something unpopular or moving forward with action that is unfamiliar and challenging. The fundamental first step toward creating health and well-being is finding the philosophy or world view that is right for us, right now. At times of shift, some return to their religious roots. Others change to a career of service or a focus on family. Courage comes in living our philosophy. The philosophy must be big enough to hold all parts of us: our inner and outer aspects. Further, it must incorporate that which is outside or beyond us—the context in which we live—the *real* world. We need a "container" of sufficient size in which to do our work.

*Changing requires us to plumb our depths honestly.* Our change must go beyond undergoing treatment for a chronic illness, changing a job or a spouse, or joining a support group. Each of these acts may be part of the shift, as long as it is associated with the deep questioning and self-discovery that enduring change requires.

Otherwise our changes will be hollow, short-lived gestures designed to gain us approval, acceptance, advancement, or safe harbor. They won't serve our core needs unless they are based on truth-telling and our personal authenticity. We don't need Band-Aids or a cover-up. We want meaningful, sustainable progress on our healing path. Our willingness to change must be deeply rooted and open to repetition because it will be challenged many times along the way. If we set the footings properly, with a personal philosophy that is strong and flexible, we'll be better prepared as each challenge or obstacle appears on our path.

A patient of mine was diagnosed with a chronic viral liver disease. The illness catalyzed a change in her philosophic viewpoint and stimulated an honest evaluation of the meaning and purpose of her life. Once she assessed the level of overpowering stress in her life, she was able to begin to bring balance to her daily existence. This required that she make life-changing decisions. The pain of staying the same was greater than the fear of changing. She was able to shift her goals from her business life to her inner life starting with small steps: lying meditation for healing, then to standing meditation to define what she was willing to stand up for, to walking meditation for problem solving. Small steps led to sustainable changes as they were integrated into her daily life. Ultimately she began a yoga class. As her insights deepened and her physical status strengthened, the results from these shifts served as ongoing motivators.

Not only were her human values affected, her lab values reflected her holistic therapy. The complementary medicine practices in partnership with her conventional care resulted in a reduction of her viral load from 32 million to undetectable over a brief period. She now calls her illness a life-changing "gift."

## Stress: Torture or Teacher?

Stress is a frequently used term these days. The word is used as a noun, verb, adjective and adverb. It is cause and it is effect. By definition, stress in the medical sense is a cascade of internal responses of the body to a threat. From an evolutionary standpoint, the threat was physical (dangerous encounter). These days it is more likely to be psychological (e.g., worry). Whether the threat is physical or psychological, real or imagined, acute or chronic, it is mediated by similar physiologic phenomena. In general terms, these bodily reactions result in increased mental alertness, heart rate, blood pressure, muscle tension, and blood sugar levels and decreased gastrointestinal (digestive) and immune system activity. Our bodies were built for short bursts of intense activity such as fleeing from a predator. When the physiologic responses become repeatedly activated, they are unsustainable and the symptoms of stress appear. The stress response is usually described as preparing us to fight, for flight, or it results in our freezing. In women it can also stimulate a nurturing or nesting response.

Symptoms of stress involve all bodily systems in a broad range of manifestations. The symptoms of stress are an expression of our body's wisdom. Actions that can save us in a brief moment of crisis, —when activated chronically by the fears of worry, memory, or expectation—become health negating rather than health creating.

Depending on the person and the circumstances, the responses/symptoms that are stress related range from clarity to panic; anxiety to depression; hyperactivity to collapse; overeating to loss of appetite; crying to rage. Stress-related illness may appear as weight gain or weight loss; diarrhea or constipation; chest pain, heart beat irregularity, shortness of breath, or dizziness.

Mental health, cardiac disease, stomach and intestinal disorders, headache, and back pain; skin problems and autoimmune diseases (chronic fatigue syndrome, fibromyalgia) are just some of the conditions demonstrated to be associated with stress. As you would expect, stress management also is a part of the comprehensive treatment plan for many illnesses. If stress isn't a contributor to the onset of a disease, it often becomes a relevant aspect of the burden of recovering from an illness.

Health status is just one of a host of precipitators of stress. Illness and injury are certainly stressors, as are birth and death and most of life's milestones and crises. Work—from starting a new job to getting a new boss, coworker, or assignment; being promoted or demoted; or retiring—is a stressor. Not having work is also a stressor. It is said that the only thing more stressful than having a job is *not* having a job. Relationships—romance, rejection, marriage, pregnancy, child-rearing, divorce, death in the family—are stressors. A major decision, decreased income, big raise or windfall, accident, or natural disaster are all stressors.

Recognizing and managing our stress can be a great source of guidance if we are aware of our body's messages to us. You'll notice all of the above are not *bad* things—just stress-evoking happenings. While the physiologic responses may be universal, the manifestations of stress in any individual are very personal and unique. The onset of a stress-related illness may be slow and subtle or sudden and alarming.

The more aware we are of the messages—the early warnings our body is sending us about how we are doing—the greater likelihood we will have of preventing a crisis or serious breakdown. Thus, the early recognition of weariness before it is complete fatigue; of subtle anxiety before it is a panic attack; of irritability before it is an angry outburst; of a heart palpitation or twinge of pain before it is a heart attack, can lead us to track the sources of our stress, modify the external causes as much as possible, and set out to rebalance our internal homeostasis (stability). This is where and how stress becomes a teacher and a healer—i.e., when we can hear the messages and are willing to act on the guidance, before breakdown occurs.

Managing stress is an arena that brings us face to face with the challenge—not of simply reducing symptoms but of changing our ways. This changing will usually involve not only our external world, but our inner world as well. This is where the potential for breakdown becomes the possibility for breakthrough.

## Facing Our Fears

Daily we face fears. Some are real. Some are creations of our minds. How do we go about facing that which we fear? Can we begin to transform our fear? We begin to transform our fear by being fully present. Being in the present reduces the fears conjured up by memories and minimizes our worry about what might happen in the future. Most fear exists in concern about the future. When you are deeply engaged in what is happening now, it is less likely that you will be immobilized with fear—even if you are in a physically dangerous situation. Fear is useful and from an evolutionary perspective has contributed to preserving the species. We are programmed to fear. It is a survival need. As is stability, which is another reason it is so hard to change.

The challenge is being discerning about what we fear. This is where choice comes in. We have the capacity to choose. Our choices can support our goal to be less fearful or they can propel us toward a life of perpetual anxiousness and worry.

As with all our reactions and responses, it is not quite as simple as choosing "a" or "b." We are defined by our genetic makeup, our upbringing and family of origin, our experiences, learnings, successes, and failures. But the possibility for growth exists through our development of awareness, insight, skill sets, and practices that move us toward discernment and away from preconceived judgments. Judgments and being judgmental render other people "wrong." It is, however, possible to disagree, hold differing opinions and to be curious without needing to make the other "wrong." This is where discernment comes into play. We are discerning when we stay open and curious as we assess a situation. It demands self-responsibility and being a fair witness.

We can build trust through the expression of appreciation, acknowledgment, respect, and understanding, and in so doing reduce fear-based behaviors. As we practice such "limbs" of love as acknowledgment, gratitude, forgiveness, and acceptance, we will feel our need to be in control lessen and appreciate the mysterious creative unfolding that we are a part of.

Over time, this practice can help reduce fear of others and of outcome. It begins with being present and tracking the source of a fear by listening to what your body is saying and from where the message is coming. This requires your quiet, undivided attention. Many meditation and affirmation practices can facilitate this tracking. Saying one's name three times, breathing into the bodily site of the fear, acknowledging that I am afraid and affirming that I can do what needs to be done can localize and ameliorate fear.

Another way of containing fear that has been described in multiple cultures is the Chiltan posture (A. Arrien, *The Four-Fold Way*). This empowerment tool is used for stabilization and containment. It is usually taught as a meditative standing or lying posture with specific positions for the hands. One hand is placed over the heart and the other hand is placed on the belly beneath the sternum/ribcage and above the navel. Practices which modulate our fears grow our courage and enhance our capacity to trust. Fear constricts us, reducing creative possibilities.

Being curious, flexible, resourceful, strong-hearted and open-hearted—all will contribute to reducing fear, stress, and overwhelm. These are character traits and their development is deep medicine.

## Happiness: A Learned Response

Reducing stress and fear are aspects of our pursuit of health. What of building on the positive and increasing happiness? Often we are seduced by the medical model of eliminating the negative, i.e., taking care of the disease. Rather than rejecting something that we don't want, we can also accentuate the positive, build on our strengths, and grow something that we do want. In their book, *What Happy People Know*, Dan Baker, Ph.D., and Cameron Stauth describe happiness qualities, tools, and traps. Happiness—the state of joy, contentment, delight—is a desired and sought-after state for most. However, we can confuse intensity, adventure, and pleasure seeking with joy, contentment, and delight.

Thus, we may look for happiness—like love—in the wrong places. The qualities of happiness include such things as being loved and loving; a sense of freedom which allows the capacity to make choices; proactivity—that is, acting rather than reacting; seeing life in a context greater than ourselves and appreciating a big picture, greater good, and higher power; and, of course, the security of health. We are aware, or at least have been warned, that we can't buy, will, demand, or mandate happiness. Once our most basic material needs have been met, it is unlikely that an increased level of happiness will be found through the external search for the perfect job, mate, home, or adventure. Neither major triumphs (e.g., winning the lottery), nor catastrophes (e.g., health or natural disasters) seem to result in a sustained, long-term (beyond about a year) change in the level of one's happiness.

True happiness seems to be more related to our state of mind than our circumstances or the impact of transitory external events. Because happiness is so directly related to our inner landscape, we can impact our level of happiness by our thoughts, emotions, and actions. What we are letting into our sacred interior by what we are watching, listening to, and talking about has an impact on our mood and level of happiness. Our food for thought must be as clean and health creating as the food we eat. That is why it is so important to do such things as read the classics and the wisdom and sacred literature from around the world, to find some daily quiet time for reflection, and to count our blessings. We must fill ourselves with the observations and advice of sages, seers, and elders, not sound bytes, hype, and advertising. At the same time, we must boundary our time of exposure to calamity-oriented, sensationalistic news, comparing our situation to others, and desiring more. All we want for our own happiness needs to be seen in the context of its impact, cost, and consequences in the big picture and in relationship to the greater good.

We can literally practice building our happiness level in these ways and learn to be happy. As we find direction through quiet introspection and constructive contribution, and are appreciated and respected for who we really are, happiness will find us. Happiness comes from feeling good (health), doing good (compassionate service), and being good (building awareness, character, values and meaningful purpose).  Growth in happiness will also lead to, or be associated with, growth in self-worth. Action that serves our state of mind, bringing us toward equanimity and contentment with regard to our inner landscape, will also change our appreciation of our external circumstances, causing us to see them differently. The reverse is not true. That is, changing our external circumstances, without doing the inner work, will not have the same impact on our inner landscape or our self-worth. As we see our selves as more worthy, we will be able to give and receive with greater ease. As cowboy, psychotherapist, philosopher, Wyatt Webb, author of *It's Not About the Horse*, says, "...you can't change an internal problem with an external solution."

### How Will Shift Occur? Tools for Change

A shift will occasionally occur suddenly, but generally takes a long time. Each of us has our own personal cadence of discovery and activity. We march to our own rhythm. For some it will be one giant step. But little steps, often separated by long, level plateaus, are more likely. Many of the steps may not seem particularly significant at the time they occur, but upon reflection, they are pivotal moves. True shift will begin with our own sincere, honest self-inquiry. Gandhi said, "Most of what you do will seem insignificant, but it is essential that you do it. We must be the change we want to see in the world."

The following tools have served me and many of my patients on the path to health.

## *Tool 1 for Change:* **Symbols and Images**

## **The Labyrinth**

The labyrinth is a representation of a step-by-step advancement along a path. When working with people seeking to change their health status, I find the labyrinth a useful image and helpful tool for catalyzing change. I encourage patients to use the walking and finger labyrinths as well as the symbolic image of the labyrinth's winding ways. A labyrinth is a path connecting outside to inside. While some forms have dead ends and therefore are mazes, one does not get lost in most labyrinths. There is a well-defined, although convoluted, way into its center and back out again. The path often turns back on itself and we frequently can't see exactly where the path is going. Symbolically, it demonstrates a route to an inner destination and one back out to where we began. This can symbolize a path to our psychological or mythological source or center. It can be a metaphor for seeking our inner or core issues that relate to our outer behavior or symptoms. We start on the outside. Here we have our habits, behaviors, symptoms, and stories. We work along the path to our interior where we encounter underlying causes and core issues.

Within our deepest selves, we can discover beliefs, fears, and character traits that underlie our external behavior, personality, or symptoms.

Our journey in the labyrinth is not complete in having reached the center of the inner circle. We must then return to the outside. We take our changes, our discoveries, and our treasure from the walk inward and return to the place on the outside of the circle where we began. Here our inner rewards can be applied in the external world.

The labyrinth is a powerful symbol of the union of our inner and outer work on the path to health and healing. Our symptoms, thoughts, feelings, and actions—from recurring patterns of behavior to acute and chronic signs and symptoms of illness— can be engaged with a practical working model that can accommodate our physical, psychological, emotional, behavioral, spiritual, and mythological dimensions.

As with all tools and symbols, we must be cautious not to romanticize the labyrinth as only a path to treasure and self-discovery. The labyrinth can also symbolize the path taken again and again— or the rut. We are in a rut when we repeat a pattern of behavior even in situations where it might no longer be appropriate. Remember the benefits we might be gaining from symptoms or behaviors: sympathy or attention. These secondary gains make it harder to change aspects of ourselves that may no longer fully serve us. Those tools and practices that show promise of helping us also carry the possibility of the opposite effect. For example, if we believe in the power of prayer, must we not also consider the power of curse?

As we contemplate change we also can ask ourselves—what is the payoff that keeps us attached to our present behavior patterns or perspective? An honest assessment of payoff helps clarify the next obstacle to be overcome along our chosen path.

## *Tool 2 for Change:* **Stories and Myths**

Much wisdom has come to us through the oral traditions of many great cultures and peoples. Stories can be healing and transforming, and can create openings and possibility. They also can immobilize us. Although stories and anecdotes are valuable tools for describing and inspiring shift, they also may serve to divert us from the less tidy and more painful work of self-investigation. In fact, our personal stories can get stuck and be repeated often to gain us sympathy and acceptance. When this occurs they are an impediment to our growth. It is vital to observe carefully what stories evoke—what memories, sensations, emotions, bodily responses, and even dreams come up in response to hearing another's story. Listen, but listen carefully. Guard against being distracted or put off, or comparing your story to someone else's. The rule of the road here is no comparison.

Our stories are important not only to us, but to those who hear them. This is particularly true when the story is revealing aspects of our inner world and is not just another description, narrative, or travelogue about our outer world. We never know what will be catalyzed in us by another's story, or when we will hold a key, through the telling of our story, for someone else.

We do not exist as individuals in a vacuum. As we travel our personal journeys, we must acknowledge our fellow travelers—the groups and communities in which we exist and by which we are powerfully influenced. We each have our ancestors and lineage. We are a part of a nuclear family, the family of man and all living beings. We are "star stuff" and part of the continuum from subatomic particles to atoms, molecules, cells, organs, and organisms. We are a citizen of a town, state, and country. We are a part of a society, culture, and religion. We are formed and defined in part by our genetic heritage and socioeconomic status.

Our personal quest for balance and wholeness includes our individual work as well as relationships within the many groups with which we are intimately involved and by which we are knowingly and unknowingly influenced. Do we live our parents' or our societies' dreams, or our own?

Our personal, individual change, while only part of the picture, is an extremely important part of the fabric of the collectives to which we belong. For each of us is a part of the critical mass necessary to effect large scale change. The myth of the hundredth monkey is one of my favorite stories about the discovery and spread of necessary change:

> "There is a phenomenon I'd like to tell you about. In it may lie our only hope of a future for our species! Here is the story of *The Hundredth Monkey*:
>
> The Japanese monkey, *Macaca fuscata*, has been observed in the wild for a period of over thirty years.

In 1952, on the island of Koshima scientists were providing monkeys with sweet potatoes dropped in the sand. The monkeys liked the taste of the raw sweet potatoes, but they found the dirt unpleasant.

An eighteen-month-old female named Imo found she could solve the problem by washing the potatoes in a nearby stream. She taught this trick to her mother. Her playmates also learned this new way and they taught their mothers, too.

This cultural innovation was gradually picked up by various monkeys before the eyes of the scientists.

Between 1952 and 1958, all the young monkeys learned to wash the sandy sweet potatoes to make them more palatable.

Only the adults who imitated their children learned this social improvement. Other adults kept eating the dirty sweet potatoes.

Then something startling took place. In the autumn of 1958, a certain number of Koshima monkeys were washing sweet potatoes—the exact number is not known. Let us suppose that when the sun rose one morning there were ninety-nine monkeys on Koshima Island who had learned to wash their sweet potatoes.

Let's further suppose that later that morning, the hundredth monkey learned to wash potatoes.

THEN IT HAPPENED!

By that evening almost everyone in the tribe was washing sweet potatoes before eating them.

The added energy of this hundredth monkey somehow created an ideological breakthrough!

But notice. A most surprising thing observed by these scientists was that the habit of washing sweet potatoes then jumped over the sea ....

Colonies of monkeys on other islands and the mainland troop of monkeys at Takasakiyama began washing their sweet potatoes!

Thus when a certain critical number achieves an awareness, this new awareness may be communicated from mind to mind.

Although the exact number may vary, the Hundredth Monkey Phenomenon means that when only a limited number of people know of a new way, it may remain the consciousness property of these people.

But there is a point at which if only one more person tunes in to a new awareness, a field is strengthened so that this awareness is picked up by almost everyone!"

**– Ken Keyes, Jr.**
*The Hundredth Monkey*

## *Tool 3 for Change:* **Dreams**

*If you don't have a dream,*
*how 'ya gonna have a dream come true?*

**– Rodgers & Hammerstein's**
South Pacific

*That which you are seeking*
*is causing you to seek.*

**– Zen Proverb**

Psychiatrist Carl Jung discovered during his mid-life crisis that he didn't know by which myth he was living. He made it his "task of tasks" to find out. When poet Donald Hall met with sculptor Henry Moore, he dared to ask Moore if he believed that there was a secret to life. "The secret of life," Moore answered, "is to have a task, something you devote your entire life to, something you bring everything to, every minute of the day for your whole life. And the most important thing is—it must be something you cannot possibly do." (from Phil Cousineau's *The Art of Pilgrimage.*)

We need to identify our dreams and longings. And we need to pursue them. We must take care not to let them be too small, lest they create a container too limited for our full flowering. Our dreams give us the energy for manifesting in the world. Our thoughts and inner life, waking and dreaming, are the sources for our deeds and actions.

Our inner and outer work are inseparable.

Dreams occur at night and during the day. In certain stages of sleep, images, emotions, and ideas occur. Daydreams may take the form of reverie or trance. A dream may be a deeply desired aspiration or something extremely beautiful or pleasant.

To dream is to consider or conceive or imagine something. "A dream is a wish your heart makes ..." according to Disney's version of Cinderella. A dreamer is one inclined to interpret experience with imagination and without strict regard to practical concerns. Dreams are a source of great inner guidance and wisdom, and a powerful first step in our process of change and healing.

It has been a dream of mine to create a healing center within contemporary, establishment medicine. I dreamed of a center that served those aspects of healing that were not necessarily visible and spoke to the needs of patients and practitioners around compassion, caring, comfort, and coping. While contemporary medicine has been very efficient in dealing with the science, mechanics, and technology of disease and treatment, it has not been as effective acknowledging and managing the fears, worry, dependency, and isolation of patients associated with their illness. Nor has it acknowledged readily or learned from other sources of knowledge and practice that can contribute to healing. Therefore, I dreamed of a center that supported practitioners who saw and served the inner and outer aspects of illness and healing in each person. A center that created an environment through design, décor, and atmosphere that fostered well-being and recovery. A dream of a real healing community. It was in my imagination that the possibility first was born that such an entity could occur.

The manifestation of my dream was realized through the commitment, discipline, and fortitude of the will. Just as hope connects our past shortcomings, failures and learnings with the future, our will connects our dreams and thoughts with action.

It is from our dreams that the fire to fight the good fight of our lives comes. We must never stop dreaming.

### On Dreaming

"We must never stop dreaming. Dreams provide nourishment for the soul, just as a meal does for the body. Many times in our lives we see our dreams shattered and our desires frustrated, but we have to continue dreaming. If we don't, our soul dies....

The good fight is the one we fight because our heart asks it of us. In the heroic ages—at the time of the knights in armor—this was easy. There were lands to conquer and much to do. Today, though, the world has changed a lot, and the good fight has shifted from the battlefields to the fields within ourselves. The good fight is the one that's fought in the name of our dreams. When we're young and our dreams first explode inside us with all of their force, we are very courageous, but we haven't yet learned how to fight. With great effort, we learn how to fight, but by then we no longer have the courage to go into combat. So we turn against ourselves and do battle within.

We become our own worst enemy. We say that our dreams are childish, or too difficult to realize, or the result of our not having known enough about life. We kill our dreams because we are afraid to fight the good fight.

The first symptom of the process of our killing our dreams is the lack of time... The busiest people I have known in my life always have enough time to do everything.

The second symptom of the death of our dreams lies in our certainties. Because we don't want to see life as a grand adventure, we begin to think of ourselves as wise and fair and correct in asking so little of life.

We look beyond the walls of our day-to-day existence, and we hear the sound of lances breaking, we smell the dust and the sweat, and we see the great defeats and the fire in the eyes of the warriors. But we never see the delight, the immense delight in the hearts of those who are engaged in the battle. For them, neither victory nor defeat is important; what's important is only that they are fighting the good fight.

And, finally, the third symptom of the passing of our dreams is peace. Life becomes a Sunday afternoon; we ask for nothing grand, and we cease to demand anything more than we are willing to give. In that state, we think of ourselves as being mature; we put aside the fantasies of our youth, and we seek personal and professional achievement.

We are surprised when people our age say that they still want this or that out of life. But really, deep in our hearts, we know that what has happened is that we have renounced the battle for our dreams—we have refused to fight the good fight.

When we renounce our dreams and find peace, we go through a short period of tranquility. But the dead dreams begin to rot within us and infect our entire being.

We become cruel to those around us, and then we begin to direct this cruelty against ourselves. That's when illness and psychosis arise. What we sought to avoid in combat— disappointment and defeat—come upon us because of cowardice. And one day, the dead spoiled dreams make it difficult to breathe, and we actually seek death. It's death that frees us from certainties, from our work, and from that terrible peace of Sunday afternoons."

**– Paulo Coelho**
*The Pilgrimage*

## *Tool 4 for Change:* **Teachers**

*Teachers open the door,*
*but you must enter by yourself.*

**– Chinese Proverb**

No one can answer our questions for us. No teacher, workshop or book—no matter how good—can eliminate the time, work, and sweat of self-inquiry. It is only through the hard work of gaining self-knowledge through trials, tribulations, quests, and journeys—the mindful experiencing and processing of what comes our way—that we can gain the insights that guide our actions and define our values on the path of our life's dream. This does not mean that teachers are not important. They are critically needed for our progress. However, no single teacher will provide all that we need over time. To quote Michael Caine's character in the film *The Quiet American,* "...you can learn a lot in a few minutes, but the rest just has to be lived." Many will touch us for varying periods. But in the end, it is up to us.

When we are ready, teachers will appear and they likely will not be in robes or speaking homilies. Rather, you will find them in the checkout line, on the freeway, or in the office. The lessons may be subtle or in-your-face. Treating everyone, even a rival, as your teacher can lead to profound learning.

A story from *Soul Food,* edited by Jack Kornfield and Christina Feldman, illustrates this:

> "A young man who had just completed his spiritual training and was eagerly intent on becoming a teacher moved to a new town. He tried to teach but no one came.

The only people with spiritual interest in the town were the many followers of a wise and well-known rabbi. Frustrated, the young teacher devised a plan to embarrass the old master and gain students for himself. He captured a small bird and one day went to where the master was seated, surrounded by many disciples.

His plan was this: if the master said the bird he held was dead he would open his hand, the bird would fly away, the master would be wrong, and the students would come to him. If the master said the bird was alive, he would quickly crush the bird in his hand and open it and say, 'See, the bird is dead.' Again the master would be wrong and the young teacher would gain students.

Holding the small bird in his hand, he spoke directly to the master. 'Tell me, if you are so wise, is this bird in my hand alive or is it dead?' The master looked back at him with great compassion and answered quite simply, 'Really, my friend, it is up to you.'"

Waiting passively for a sudden shift makes little sense if we are responding to the rumblings within that are beckoning us to heal.

Rather, we can choose to embark on a path to shift our perception. To start this shift toward a health-generating foundation, we need to be our own teacher and take ourselves to our own personal school of self-knowledge and complete our homework.

Your first study session will require little more than a quiet place and a brief period of uninterrupted time to begin to pursue an intimacy with yourself. Anticipate this first date evolving into a daily appointment with yourself as you explore your heartfelt desires and needs. In these interludes with self, you will be both patient and healer.

What is critical to appreciate about tools is that in order for them to contribute to dreamed of or desired change and healing, they must be *used!* Many of us are very good at collecting tools, plans, and programs from many sources, but we are less good at using those tools. Many tools of change are time tested, of known effectiveness, and evidence based. If they are not utilized, if we do not practice what we are taught, our "muscles" will not grow, our skill set will not improve, our potential will not be realized. It is not only ourselves who are missing out when we don't realize our potential. Our personal work of change and healing has impact beyond ourselves. We influence our intimate contacts and our communities by our personal growth. As we change, our world changes. Our personal wellness contributes to the public health and to planetary healing.

---

⌘ **Exercise for Step Two:** ⌘
**Breakdown or Breakthrough**

---

To begin to build a philosophic foundation for health and change and to identify aspects of your life which may be calling for a shift, ask yourself the following questions:

- Why am I here?
- What are some of the milestone events that have led me to where I am today?
- What is the meaning of my life?
- What is the purpose of my life?
- Am I living in ways that are consistent with the meaning and purpose of my life?
- What is my calling?
- What are the values that govern my life?
- What is my life's dream?
- What are my gifts? My talents? How can I bring them forward?
- What do I need?
- What are the resources available to me?
- What are the obstacles that I am presently facing?
- What can I do in the next...
  - ✓ 24 hours
  - ✓ 1 week
  - ✓ 1 month
  - ✓ 6 months
  - ✓ 1 year
  - ✓ 5 years

  ...to begin to effect change and move toward my goal?

Answering questions like these is challenging. It requires honesty and causes discomfort. We all want to look good and avoid discomfort and get over it quickly. The hard questions seem ill-defined and unanswerable. We wish for some multiple-choice options!

As we get more comfortable with the process—practice—it will get easier. We will realize that the answers are less important than good questions. The good question is more important than the seemingly right answer. So continue to inquire and ask and carry with you the good question. The questions and the answers will change, but the work of authentic inquiry will continue to reward.

An upset student who had just completed a particularly rigorous exam approached Albert Einstein. The student complained, "Professor Einstein, the questions on this year's final exam were the same as last year's!"

"Don't worry," replied Einstein, "the answers are different."

In which of the following "domains" of life are you feeling "stressed"?
- Health
- Relationship
- Work
- Sense of Abundance, Prosperity, Resources

What are your identifiable "stressors"? Devise a plan for your external and internal stress management.

What does your talk tell you about your readiness to change? Is it "change talk" or "resistance talk"?

*If you look to others for fulfillment,*
*you will never truly be fulfilled.*
*If your happiness depends on money,*
*you will never be happy with yourself.*
*Be content with what you have;*
*rejoice in the way things are.*
*When you realize there is nothing lacking,*
*The whole world belongs to you.*

**– Lao Tzu**
Tao Te Ching

## Step Three

# Searching for a Metaphor:
# If You Can Name It,
# You Can Change It,
# If You Act On It

NOBODY SEES A FLOWER,
REALLY -- IT IS SO SMALL --
WE HAVEN'T TIME, LIKE TO
HAVE A FRIEND TAKES TIME.

*GEORGIA O'KEEFFE*

*To see the World in a grain of sand,*
*and Heaven in a wild flower,*

*Hold infinity in the palm of your hand,*
*And eternity in an hour.*

**– William Blake**
The Little Zen Companion

How we describe or name something has tremendous power and carries great meaning. Naming, identifying, observing, describing, and tracking are early necessities if we intend to change something. While we understand that "the menu is not the meal" and "the map is not the territory," mere mention of many words catalyzes a response as full blown as the actual item. Many of us would rather dive into the activity described as a "piece of cake" than the one called a "tough nut to crack." We would rather hike the trail called Morning Glory than the one designated Widow Maker, regardless of the actual nature of the terrain.

Naming and categorizing affect the way we view health and healing, with far-reaching impact. To date, Americans have typically conceived of their healthcare in two ways: the battlefield and the marketplace. Both of these metaphors for perceiving health have powerful implications.

## The Battlefield

In the battlefield metaphor, disease is the enemy; doctors, nurses, and other healthcare professionals are soldiers; and our bodies are the battlegrounds. The arsenal is the medication and technology employed. We wage war against cancer. We fight heart disease, wipe out resistant infections, advance battle lines and frontiers. These are harsh images, often difficult to accept when dealing with infirmity, death, and the birthing of new life.

Early in my surgical career, I operated on a lovely woman with a large malignant tumor located next to and behind one of her eyes. The surgery was very extensive requiring removal of her eye and all the tissues around it in the eye socket. It was an aggressive operation for an aggressive malignancy. Fortunately the tumor was completely removed.

Because of the risk of tumor spread, the group of specialists who reviewed her situation recommended X-ray therapy but not chemotherapy as part of the post-surgical management. At an early post-operative visit with my patient, I described the results of the surgery and the expert panel's recommendations. I discussed the "battle plan" with the intention of conveying the positive aspects of the treatment plan in this very serious situation.

Two days later, the patient's sister called me saying the patient had been devastated by our visit. Her sister wanted to know what had happened. I had *conveyed* the "plan of attack" and expressed that we were in a good place in very tough circumstances. My patient, however, had *heard* that there was no need to do chemotherapy as there was no value in that treatment because there was no possibility of containing the tumor. Unintentionally I had taken away her hope while describing the tactics for the battle against her cancer. My sensitivity to the battlefield metaphor was forever changed, as was my capacity to insure that hope was always carefully woven into my prognosis.

Despite the potential incongruities, there is no question that the image of the good fight has an important place in our healing vocabulary. But often the best general wins by negotiation, not in battle. The best healer is not always the one running about attempting cures of disease, but the little-seen practitioner who is preventing illness.

In *The Art of War*, Sun Tzu draws parallels between the healing arts and the martial arts. He demonstrates that both healing and martial arts involve dealing with disharmony and change.

In both, knowledge of the problem is the key to solutions. Ideal strategies accomplish the most by doing the least early rather than the most later—"An ounce of prevention is worth a pound of cure."

He teaches us to be prudent but not hesitant; to take calculated risks but not needless ones; to adapt to existing, changing situations the way water adapts to the contours of the ground; and that yielding and retreat may well be necessary as part of a larger plan and deeper purpose.

### The Marketplace

In the second metaphor, the marketplace, health is a commodity. What it means, according to *Webster's Dictionary*, is that health becomes an article of trade or commerce. Patients become consumers, clients, and managed lives. Hospitals and clinics become providers, while insurance companies and health maintenance organizations become payers. In this picture, lines of revenue, cost centers, quarterly profits, and books of business come to dominate.

We must acknowledge the cost of our healthcare practices, but we can't allow these fiscal implications to overshadow our needs as humans. We must still care for our young, our sick, and our elderly. The fiscal and material constraints to our health and healing practices are real, and must be recognized and incorporated into affordable practices. We must also acknowledge those aspects of our existence that are nonmaterial if our practice is to be enduring.

Finances alone cannot be permitted to drive a realm so fraught with the complexities of being human.

While it may be the time to discontinue life support, not perform a particular surgical procedure, or use a specialized technologic innovation, these decisions are medical, ethical, moral, social, and theological and should not be only financial and economic if we are to compassionately deal with the very young, very old, and very sick.

Though useful, both the battlefield and marketplace approaches to health and healing are limiting. For a complete vision of health, we need a new metaphor that incorporates a fresh vocabulary and new reference points for health.

## Ecology—A New Metaphor for Health

*If Congress is ever to make meaningful progress in reforming our fast-changing system for financing and delivering medical care, a new way must be found to think about health itself. This will require at least a new metaphoric framework that permits us to re-envision and thus to reconstruct the American medical care system. I suggest that the leading candidate for a new metaphor is ecology.*

**– George J. Annas, J.D., M.P.H.**

An ecology metaphor for health and medicine has been a long time coming. Its roots go back to the 1700s with physician and geologist James Hutton, who proposed the specialty of planetary medicine. Hutton thought species-specific medicine—that is, medical practices dealing only with the human species—was too small. He thought that if we did not take into consideration all else that surrounded us and co-existed with us on the planet, we couldn't properly diagnose or treat any malady.

Ecology is the study of the relationship among living organisms and their environments. Using the wisdom of nature as a guide, the ecologic metaphor offers us a workable and sustainable approach to health that incorporates the scientific and the spiritual, the individual and the planetary. The key principles of an ecologic metaphor include:

- *Evolution/co-evolution:* We are in a state of constant flow and change.
- *Interdependence:* Our existence is a part of a larger web of life with complex interactions and feedback loops.
- *Limits:* We have definite boundaries and limited resources. We must seek that which is sustainable.
- *Diversity:* Every part of the whole is a unique and essential contribution.
- *Cycles:* Our existence is a part of nature's cyclical patterns.

– Adapted from **Principles of Ecology**
Center for Ecoliteracy, Berkeley, California

## Using the Ecology Metaphor

Using this metaphor, disease becomes an imbalance, the work of the physician is stewardship, healing becomes part of the process of change, and the hospital is part of a larger ecosystem.

Ecological systems are driven by evolution—the process of change over time. In the 4.6 billion years since the earth formed, climates have changed, land masses moved, and species have come and gone. Change is our reality.

The ecological metaphor also reminds us we're all in it together! Push here, something bulges over there. Pour toxic waste in the sewer drain and it shows up in the bay to be consumed in tomorrow night's seafood buffet. Grow too many crops without revitalizing the soil and decreasing yields can be expected. Overgraze a field, and the soil will erode; the stock will subsequently go hungry, as will the human population waiting for them to go to market. As environmentalist John Muir said, "...everything is hitched to everything else."

A state of dynamic balance with constant modulation results from this interrelatedness and interdependence. Physiologically this intricate balance is called homeostasis and is maintained via feedback loops of communication. When blood sugar levels fall, we experience the sensation of hunger and want something to eat. In an ecosystem, when herd size exceeds the capacity, starvation and illness ensue, adjusting the herd size to sustainable levels.

Small and subtle variances may lead to large disruptions. A tiny plaque in a coronary artery can cause a massive heart attack. A small embolus to a blood vessel in the brain can result in a stroke, or "brain attack." A minimal change in water quality or quantity can upset plant and animal productivity and health. Relatedness is not confined to a specific location. Our common ancestry and humanity link us over great distances. In a sense, our compassion for the starving in Africa or sick in India has roots in our shared origins and planetary linkages.

That we live within limits is all too clear to us after payday when we try to balance our checkbooks. We feel these limits from family budgets all the way to Washington, D.C. Ultimately, it is our planet that sets the limits. We survive because of our location in relationship to the sun, and on limited earthly resources.

An understanding of how public allocations are spent becomes much broader when viewed from an ecologic perspective. Our society can't afford to develop every potential technologic advance and can't afford to transplant a new kidney into everyone with renal failure. We must prioritize within real limits. Just as we must decide whether we can afford prisons, housing, and schools, we must make choices on our path to health. Describing our health within an ecological context will help us distribute our resources, recognize our limits, find balance, and accept compromise.

Variations within and among species are essential. Every part of the whole matters. Our bodies require a diverse population of cells, tissues and organs. All are essential to our healthy functioning. Brain, heart, muscle, bone, and blood—all must work in concert toward the greater good.

Diversity lends stability and survival potential to the fabric of the natural world. The devastating famine in Ireland was due to failure of a homogenous non-diversified potato crop. The bigger the potential storehouse of solutions, the broader the range of problems that can be encountered successfully. Nature's capacity for innovative solutions lies in its diversity. Fortunately, the possibilities for creating health are much more akin to a rainforest than a monoculture. Recognizing the value of variation in the natural world can help us value the diversity of human experience, background, culture, race, age, opinion, and solution. Open to multiple possibilities, we open options on our own path to health.

Each one of us represents a combination of factors never before seen together and never to be seen again. The recognition and acceptance of our own uniqueness gives us the potential to accept the differences of other individuals and groups.

Just as exhalation follows inhalation, digestion follows ingestion, night follows day, and death follows life, our existence is a part of nature's cyclical patterns. Understanding this offers us a chance to come to terms with the transitory nature of health.

Each moment of life, we experience the pumping of the heart, the flow of the blood, the rhythm of our breathing. On an ecological level, the planetary pulse brings us the cycles of night and day, the monthly movement of the moon around the earth, and the seasonal variations of winter, spring, summer, and fall with their attendant preparation, budding, blooming, and harvest. The cycles of birth, growth, aging, death, and decay are natural phenomena to be understood and accepted. The same patterns of endings, new beginnings, and transitions fill our personal and professional lives.

How long do we try to fight off the natural consequences of aging in the name of good health? How long do we postpone death in the name of modern medical science? How long do we delay a needed ending and fresh start? Accept these cycles! And let us not forget the pause between inhalation and exhalation, the space between each pulsation felt at the wrist, the respite of a night's sleep. We need rest between bursts of activity whether in a momentary, daily, monthly, or yearly cycle.

## Believing Is Seeing

The model or metaphor that we choose to frame a question or view an issue will often determine the answer or definition. The following story illustrates this point (its health implications notwithstanding).

Two priests were discussing the appropriateness of praying and smoking at the same time. Because they were unable to resolve the issues themselves, they decided to seek out the bishop, which they did independently. When the two priests were next together they reported that they had talked to the bishop about smoking and praying.

Interestingly, one had been told it was okay to both smoke and pray at the same time. The other had been told that it was not okay.

Puzzled, the priests asked each other how the question was posed. The priest who received the negative response had asked if it was okay to smoke while praying. The priest who had received the affirmative response had asked if it was okay to pray while smoking!

According to a well-known Talmudic saying, we do not see things as they are; we see them rather as we are. If we see our daily activities as a struggle or battle, they are likely to be exactly that. If, however, we make the choice to see our daily lives as a dance, we'll be dealing with dancing shoes and partners instead of combat boots and enemies.

## Summer Wake Up

Sometimes it is very difficult to see ourselves clearly. It is quite interesting that we can only see ourselves in a mirror (reflecting glass) or as we are mirrored back to ourselves by others who are responding or reacting to us in one way or another. Smiles, hugs, and nodding are welcome reflections, while looking or turning away, grimacing, argument, or avoidance are ways we would rather not be reflected back.

Not long ago, my wife Susy and I arrived in British Columbia, Canada, for a summer holiday. This is an annual summer pilgrimage for us. We arrived tired, as usual, after the long drive from San Francisco and the multiple ferry boat lineups and crossings to reach our sylvan island destination. Since our previous visit eleven months earlier, our work, travel, family, and social schedules had been full, like those of most people choosing to read this book.

The year had been rewarding, stimulating, and meaningful. I had not been ill, did not feel burned out, stressed out, or on the verge. I knew that I was ready for summer vacation—a ritual I have loved since childhood and the countdown until school was out. I work hard, but I also ensure some down time, practice yoga regularly, walk daily, exercise vigorously at least one weekend day, and try to practice what I preach. I was ready for a vacation, but not prepared for what followed our weary but anticipatory arrival. The bottom fell out!

I slept ten to twelve hours each night and looked forward to my afternoon nap. I could sleep inside, outside, on a bed, in a hammock, or in a chair. Vertical activities—such as hiking and biking—were fine in short bursts and as long as they didn't interfere with my horizontal needs of sleep, naps, and rest periods.

My belly responded with an untwisting complete with gurgling, cramps, and loss of appetite.

My dreams, both day and night, were vivid, imaginative, and full of possible explanations for my symptoms—most of them dark and distressing.

After several days as my body rested, my sleep modulated. My recovery was not as rapid as my collapse and I was determined to see beyond the symptoms even as they improved. Obviously, I had been exhausted but failed to recognize or admit it. Or I had simply overridden my needs. How had I been so blind, deaf, and oblivious to my own situation? I had clearly ignored or denied visceral messages about my state of well-being. "What was the message in this experience? What was the meaning?" I asked myself.

Even as an astute, knowledgeable doctor trained to see symptoms and warning signs in others, trained to name things accurately, my self-seeing and my inner vision were blurred, clouded, and fraught with blind spots.

My self-hearing and inner listening were dulled, deficient, and reduced. I had not been fully present or current with myself. I had not named or diagnosed myself well, and so I couldn't take care of myself well.

I did have a waking-up experience after my restful vacation. I did not want to go back to sleep or ignore the wake-up call. I wanted to see my episode literally and metaphorically. I was afforded an opportunity to untangle my "inner laundry" before the washing machine broke down or the contents became so tightly knotted that they were impossible to unravel. I had let go of what I didn't even appreciate I was holding and hiding. I looked and listened again after I was forced to stop by my exhaustion.

Isn't that what we have been instructed to do at corners, turns, and crossroads since we were children? "Stop! Look! Listen!" The advice is still useful. I stop, look, and listen regularly.

Redefine the schedule, rebalance the work load, and insure that incremental relief is afforded for solitude, contemplation, quiet time with family. I revisit my motivation, fears, and insecurities and insure priorities and pacing that are sustainable. This often requires that I remind myself that whatever I am concerned or worried about is likely not really as important as I think it is.

I know that as a healer it is necessary that I diagnose myself impeccably and that the naming of my status and conditions reflects what is true. Otherwise, how can I be of service to others?

Our choice of metaphor through which to view health and healing becomes an integral part of the healing itself. The metaphor of ecology builds on the understanding and insight gained through scientific as well as spiritual inquiry. Furthermore, the ecological principles have application beyond our human boundaries.

The ecology metaphor has the breadth and depth for a subject as expansive as health and healing. The ecological perspective does not imply that challenges to our understanding will be eliminated, that difficult decisions won't be necessary, that no compromises will be required, or that everyone will be satisfied or happy all the time. It does, however, help to create a set of ground rules for meeting the challenges of creating our personal health and contributing to the well-being of our environments. Naming that which we desire to change accurately and fully, just like making the correct diagnosis, is an important step in the practice of deep medicine.

If we are naming only the external or superficial (symptoms) without identifying associated underlying related aspects (emotions, needs, desires, beliefs) our treatment and changes have a much lower likelihood of succeeding. The treatment must be a proper one or we will not be valuable physicians to ourselves or others. Precise naming and choice of metaphor are essential so that we accurately identify what is and act appropriately.

⌘                **Exercise for Step Three:**                ⌘
**Literally and Figuratively**

To explore the ecology metaphor of health and
healing:

Consider this story of interdependent cause and
effect relationships among a diverse set of creatures
that were disrupted and what happened.

> "Over forty years ago, scientists in Borneo
> sprayed DDT in an effort to control
> mosquitoes responsible for a major malaria
> outbreak. A couple of weeks after local
> swamps were sprayed, the thatch roofs of the
> area's huts began to collapse, one by one. At
> first, no one could understand why. After a
> while, the mystery was explained.
>
> As they had intended, the scientists had
> sprayed the mosquitoes and killed them.
> However, the DDT also contaminated
> houseflies, which were resistant to the
> pesticide. Later, geckos, which eat flies and
> thatch caterpillars, began to die from the
> poisonous flies. Since the caterpillars no
> longer had a natural predator, their
> population boomed. As the caterpillars,
> which dine on thatch, made their way to the
> village huts, thatch roofs began to dissolve
> under swarms of caterpillars whose
> population was growing out of control.
>
> Furthermore, sick geckos, slowed by the
> poison, were easy prey for Borneo's cats. As

the cats ate the geckos, they too began to accumulate DDT and die.

The decreasing cat population enabled the area's rats to proliferate. The increase in the rat population resulted in a deadly risk of bubonic plague, which is carried by rat fleas. To prevent an outbreak of the plague, scientists finally resorted to desperate measures.

Cats were airlifted to the region and parachuted in to replace the depleted feline population, restoring balance to the local ecosystem and health to the region."

**– Ray Peterson**
Biologist, Audubon Canyon Ranch
Marin County, California

We are familiar with the diversity of race, culture, religion, sex, age and ability. The ultimate diversity resides in our own unique individual "differentness." How does the recognition of your own differentness impact your potential for accepting the differences of others?

Having considered the unique differences we all exhibit, remember all humans have the same number of bones and teeth, similar blood types and the genetic capacity to mate among all races and cultures.

- Do any two humans have the same fingerprint?
- Do any two humans make the same contribution to the world?

Consider how our naming, judgments, and descriptions of people and things impact our behavior toward them. For example, someone acting angry and hostile toward you could be called an aggressive monster or a human being with great suffering. How might your behavior differ given these contrasting namings?

Learn of several plants that affect human health—from common or exotic sources. [*Hint:* Some diseases that have botanical treatments include heart disease (foxglove), cancer (yew trees), mental illness (St. John's Wort), digestive problems (ginger), and the common cold (Echinacea, garlic, goldenseal)]. Link this question to the issues of tropical rainforest destruction.

Consider a tree. An ecologic metaphor on whose branches, visible for all to see, are its sunlight-collecting leaves and flowers and fruits. We might be tempted to call these visible parts the results of the tree's labors. If we were only to pay attention to these results or outcomes, we would ignore the roots. The roots, not seen and deep under the ground, connect the tree to its life sources of soil and water. Beneath the outer bark, transport of these nutrients occurs. A tree or plant is a beautiful and brilliant example/ image of the elemental and essential connection between the seen and unseen, inner and outer, input and results.

## Step Four

# Bridging the Gap:
# Balancing Opposites and
# Holding Paradox

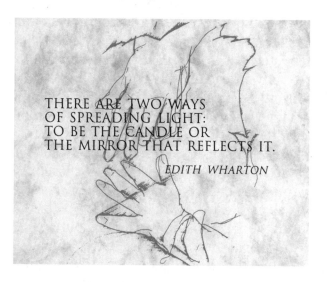

THERE ARE TWO WAYS
OF SPREADING LIGHT:
TO BE THE CANDLE OR
THE MIRROR THAT REFLECTS IT.

*EDITH WHARTON*

*The most beautifying and deepest experience one can have is the sense of the mysterious. It is the underlying principle of religion as well as of serious endeavors in art and science.*

**– Albert Einstein**

*We shall accomplish nothing at all if we divide our world and our lives into two domains; one of the sacred and the other governed by the laws of economics, politics, and the simple self-assertion of the group...stopping ones ears so as not to hear the voice from above is breaking the connection between existence and the meaning of existence.*

**– Martin Buber**

My work as a surgeon placed me at the interface of science and spirit in my professional life. On the one hand, surgery is a precise anatomical and technological activity demanding the best science can offer. On the other hand, it is a priestly activity supported by ritual, including hand-washing and wearing ceremonial gowns. The trusting patient, anesthetized upon the operating table, gives himself or herself over to the surgical team. The cold stainless steel blade pierces the flesh, which allows entry to the hallowed bodily core. Probing exploration, excision of diseased tissue, and repair of injury occur amid the pulsing warmth of bodily organs and fluids. The surgeon is not only a technician of the flesh, but an instrument of healing and of care. The healing impact of the surgeon's kind words, eye contact, smile, and gentle touch has a power as do the knife and laser.

Surgical analysis is dominated by outer structure and attention to form. In the Chinese construct, the whole is made up of yin and yang, which are poles that paradoxically oppose and complement each other. Outer manifestations are yang. This external and explicit reality is accompanied by yin, the inner and implicit dimension. Yin characteristics reflect process and the receptive, intuitive, and mysterious sides of things. Yin and yang communication styles are different. Yang talks and yin listens. Relating the two is at the heart of relationship. Seeing yin and yang as well as their relationship is essential to seeing wholeness.

Our lives, like surgical practice, are not limited to the external yang confines. As we evolve as healers and humans, we are carried to the vast frontiers of our invisible, inner yin landscape. The yin-yang and scientific-sacred models do not require us to be a scientist or theologian to appreciate this juxtaposition of worlds. Our healing work gives each of us the opportunity to merge facts, techniques, and caring. For ourselves we can make the shift to bring the secular and sacred visibly together on a daily basis.

## The Power of Paradox

A paradox is a seemingly contradictory statement. Generally paradox relates to a truth, the opposite of which is also true. Paradox is often represented by extremes, dualities, or opposites that turn out to be connected: dark/light, up/down, left/right, inner/outer, logical/emotional, pain/pleasure, rich/poor. The two-edged sword, yin and yang, subjective and objective, and many other examples represent the dilemma posed by duality and paradox.

When I was a high school student, the tension between creationists and evolutionists stimulated me to come to terms with this particular paradox. I did so through writing a position paper bringing together the Book of Genesis and Darwin's Theory of Evolution. In true sophomoric fashion, I posited that if we were only to conceive of the length of the days of creation as not being limited to a mere twenty-four hours, but of being much longer—epochal length actually—then we could braid the theory of evolution and the biblical explanation of creation. While this explanation may not be suitable for many, it served my needs. The paper presented a conundrum around the dissonance/discrepancy between two differing points of view.

By engaging this dissonance and the struggle to merge two opposing positions, I brought something very difficult to understand into a construct that made sense to me. I found a relationship with the mystery of creation that continues to serve me. This was a compromise around a synthesis that acknowledged the difficulty—actually the discomfort or pain—that is associated with trying to explain the unexplainable.

This early step in dealing with paradox began a lifelong relationship with holding opposites that has been healing for me. Since it reduced the suffering of being unable to fully understand reality—i.e., what is—it was healing. A significant part of healing is reducing pain and suffering. And part of healing is coming to terms with and holding the creative tension of paradox.

Science may act as though it does not need mysticism, and mysticism may seem as though it does not need science; but humanity needs both. Science and spirit are bridged by unseen connections that exist at the frontiers of what is known and what is unknown. Science is a powerful and flexible instrument in our search for health and in our search for truth. Knowledge and skills broaden as new information becomes available through careful method and rigorous, repeatable observation and experimentation. When scientists become rigid and inflexible, their work is no longer science but dogma or edict. True science is curious and flexible, encouraging growth and change. Present limits are temporary boundaries to the mysteries of what lies beyond that which is known.

## Beyond the Known

The personal quest for health brings us face to face with many dilemmas and paradoxes. There are splits or separations that might not represent accurate interpretations of the world. Examples include the alleged antagonism between science and religion, evolution and creationists, left brain and right brain, rational and intuitive, and technological and romantic. This simplistic either/or mindset must be resisted. Rather, extremes should be viewed as perceived ends of a large continuum. At the same time we are not only ashes and dust, but also the highest conscious expression of billions of years of creation unfolding.

Even the largest realities can be unseen. The sun is still there even though obscured by clouds, as is a mountain enshrouded in fog. Our understanding of "seeing" must extend beyond the physical—outside the visible spectrum of electromagnetic energy. As Antoine de Saint Exupéry said, "It is only with the heart that one can see rightly; what is essential is invisible to the eye." This awareness opens new realms of possibility.

What lies past the range of our largest telescope? What might be seen if there were more power of magnification in our strongest microscope? These questions touch the hows and whys of our existence, where scientific fact blends with spiritual issues of source and meaning. For a society most comfortable with the objective, impersonal, and technical facts, the subjective aspects of the world show us limits and vulnerabilities. This can induce anxiety. But our path to health mandates opening ourselves to this unknown.

We can't do our work only when it is easy. As
the precious pearl is well encased in a protective
shell, we must venture where it is dark and messy
and difficult.

## Meeting Places

Contemporary medicine may be the bridge, the
interface, between the best of applied science and
the deepest questions about the meaning of our
existence. For here, we bring together our sacred,
soulful parts with our physical, material, and
rational parts. Here the elements of our spirituality
are brought into play. Our faith, belief systems, and
capacity to trust are tested as we are tested by
illness, ordeal, and infirmity. Nonmaterial values
are called into high relief as the value of our material
possessions pales next to the gift of health.

The power of subjective experience and the
texture and resilience of our spirituality often
inform us with greater accuracy than facts and
figures about what we need to know in order to
make health-related decisions for ourselves and our
loved ones. Our connectedness to all around us
through joy, sorrow, empathy, sympathy, and
shared human experience becomes increasingly
clear. John Astin, Ph.D., of the California Pacific
Medical Center, San Francisco, evaluated why
patients use alternative medicine. He pointed out
that in alternative therapies patients find "...an
acknowledgment of the importance of treating
illness within a larger context of spirituality and life
meaning... The use of alternative care is part of a
broader value orientation and set of cultural beliefs,
one that embraces a holistic, spiritual orientation to
life."

If grandma is on a respirator in the intensive care unit, many facts and figures such as cost of care, chances for survival, and insurance coverage will contribute to the decision as to if and when the respirator and support services are discontinued. In the end, however, it is likely that her love of life, her wishes, desires, and her family's weighing of her pain and suffering will be most critical in the decision-making process.

As we become more comfortable at this meeting place of the scientific and spiritual, even some of the most basic scientific tenets can be understood as having profound spiritual as well as rational implications.

Cosmologist Brian Swimme and Father Thomas Berry, in their book *The Universe Story*, wed contemporary scientific understanding and the world's great wisdom traditions in describing 15 billion years of cosmic existence. They recount the story of the universe as science and myth, blending geological and biological findings with man's search for meaning. One example they give pertains to Einstein's famous formula, energy equals mass times the speed of light squared ($E=mc^2$).

This is pure science—physics and mathematics. It also represents a powerful spiritual truth: energy and matter are the same. What else is there on the planet but energy and matter in their various forms? Here is scientific corroboration of the interconnectedness of all on our planet.

Not unlike the phenomena of astral bodies such as black holes, white holes, and the theories of particle physics, we are in a constant state of interplay with our surroundings. Recognizing that what we perceive as energy (light, sound, electromagnetic force) and what we perceive as matter (animal, vegetable, mineral, gas, solid, liquid) are related and are in a state of constant flow (movement, interchange) is a profound lesson.

Swimme and Berry also wed science and spirit in discussing the Big Bang. This theory of our planet's origin is a well-regarded explanation of the birth of the planets and solar system from an explosion of hot gases in the vastness of space billions of years ago. The evidence, of course, is fragmentary and circumstantial since there were no witnesses. Nonetheless, it is an explanation that stands—and is believed by many—until one better comes along. But let us not be too smug about the scientific explanation of the origins of our planetary home. Legends, stories, and creation myths—from Genesis to the origin myths of indigenous peoples all over the world—are more meaningful for many.

Quantum physics and particle theory also beg spiritual questions. Gary Zukav in *The Dancing Wu Li Masters* and Fritjof Capra in *The Tao of Physics* both support the relationship between science and the sacred and the visible and invisible worlds. Physics, chemistry, and mathematics have taught us that our atomic structure and the basic particles of which we are made—protons, neutrons, and electrons—are identical to those found in all organic and inorganic substances.

The chemical elements (including carbon, hydrogen, and oxygen) and compounds (such as water and salt) are ubiquitous in nature. At a molecular level, significant quantities of DNA are shared—even by very different species.

Our understanding of empty and solid is also brought into question by the scientific explanation of our makeup. Although our sensory perception tells us we stop at our skin, our atomic particles are not so neatly bound. Relative to the size of the building block particles, there are vast distances of space between particles: like planets and stars in the far reaches of outer space. We are more empty than solid! Nonetheless, when we sit in a chair, it supports our weight, and we cannot walk through a wall in spite of the inherent open space that resides within.

Science brings to light the dynamism and impermanence of our human condition. It is the state of our existence, balanced on the cusp of energy and matter, full of emptiness and in constant flow. The breakfast we ate this morning becomes the energy that fuels our bodies, just as an acorn gains energy from sun, soil, and water. The acorn expresses its potential by becoming the tree that yields the log, that feeds the fire that warms our bodies, that leaves the ash that returns to soil once again to feed the interconnected, interdependent cycle—of which we are a part.

There is much to cycles of birth and death that eludes scientific explanation and leaves us with penetrating questions about the origins of creation and its unfolding. These questions bring the mystics, mathematicians, philosophers, and physicists together in search of answers at the shorelines of scientific inquiry and philosophic dialogue. It is here the scientific and the sacred are seen as inseparable partners in the cosmic dance. These questions form the bridge between the explicit, objective, rational, and material—and the realm of the nonmaterial, the implicit, subjective and invisible.

## Healing with Science and Spirit

The inner, invisible world refers to those aspects of us that might not be discovered by the physician's use of direct observation, palpation, percussion, or auscultation. I allude to those recesses of our being that are not necessarily accessed by the usual questions asked by your doctor relating to chief complaint, history of present or past illnesses, and systems review. It is the territory of questions such as: Why am I here? What does it mean? And, what purposes do I serve?

The inner world is where our own self-knowledge and identity and creative purpose are formed upon the landscape of faith and fear, worry and wishes, dreams and disappointments, joy and sadness, intuition and coincidence, grief and belief, and inspiration and imagination. This territory lacks a map, but it is there. It is as real as it is fantasy-like. And though it seems near, it is also remote. We engage it in many ways, from absolution to Zen.

We behold this inner world and contemplate, meditate, and pray. We seek to quiet the daily busy work and chatter to access the inner stillness and wisdom. There are different names for this hidden sphere: the individual soul, the realm of spirit, and the infinite. It is experienced through awe and mystery. Language in this realm is abstract and the concepts nebulous. Nonetheless, the inner world has a powerful impact on our outer world.

"If we become addicted to the external, our interiority will haunt us. We will become hungry with a hunger no image, person, or deed can still. To be wholesome, we must remain truthful to our vulnerable complexity.

In order to keep our balance, we need to hold the interior and exterior, visible and invisible, known and unknown, temporal and eternal, ancient and new together. No one else can undertake this task for you. You are the one and the only threshold of an inner world. This wholesomeness is holiness. To be holy is to be natural, to befriend the worlds that come to balance in you. Behind the façade of image and distraction, each person is an artist in this primal and inescapable sense. Each one of us is doomed and privileged to be an inner artist who carries and shapes a unique world."

**– John O'Donohue**
*Anam Cara: A Book of Celtic Wisdom*

By coming to terms with paradox and opposites, we bring ourselves a step closer to practicing deep medicine. Seeing the continuum between what initially appears to be opposites is part of seeing the whole in which we exist. We can learn as much from a small child as a great teacher. We can benefit from our failures as well as our successes. Too much food can be as bad for our health as not enough food. We cherish, seek, and value the heroic—is not the humdrum as important?

We want everyone to respect and honor us—do we show respect and honor to everyone? Not enough physical activity is not good for our well-being and neither is too much. Neither too much nor not enough of anything is the ideal. As we study the extremes, we learn the power of the middle way. We appreciate the creative possibility that lies in the realm between the polar opposites.

   This appreciation is a step toward balance—placing us not in the extremes of positionality or rigid thinking, but rather in the center place of moderation and creativity. We move from the place of potential disequilibrium on either end of the teeter-totter to the center and equilibrium. This is the place of balance—and balance is health. This is the place of accepting the whole—and wholeness is health. This is deep medicine.

## ⌘        Exercise for Step Four:        ⌘
## Building Bridges

Reflect on the following questions and add several of your own that define the boundaries, contact points, and interplay between the so-called paradoxes of: (1) the scientific and sacred, (2) the rational and irrational, (3) the visible and invisible, and (4) the technologic and romantic.

- What occurs before birth?
- What happens after death?
- Is birth the polar opposite of death, or is life the opposite?
- Where is the anatomic location of the soul/mind/consciousness?
- What are the history and potential residing in a seed?
- What do the powerful journeys of life characterized by seasonal animal migrations represent?
- How can all snowflakes be hexagons, yet no two are alike?
- Consider the expansiveness and complexity of the pathways that brought your breakfast to your table this morning.
- Reflect on how your work puts you at the interface of the secular and the sacred.
- What does it mean to you to be "centered"?
- What does it mean to you to be "in right placement"?

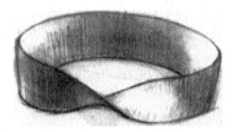

A Mobius Strip is a continuous surface that is formed from a rectangular strip (e.g., a piece of paper) by rotating one end 180 degrees and attaching it to the other end. It is a common symbol for infinity, and it is named after German astronomer and mathematician August Mobius (1790–1868). It is a scientific construct that stretches the imagination at the junction of the finite and infinite. The Mobius Strip is another tangible model of the continuous connection between inner and outer aspects and the relationship between seemingly different edges. Make a Mobius Strip from a piece of paper approximately 1" wide by 10" long. Track a line starting on one of the surfaces until you return to your starting point. Track the edge of the strip.

How do your findings relate to your life?

## Connecting with Paradox:  Unifying Duality

The dualities that seem to exist on our planet are quite interesting, curious, and instructive. It is noteworthy how it is necessary for male and female parts ("opposites"?) to come together to biologically reproduce the/any species. Is this the ultimate duality? Doesn't it have a paradoxical quality about it? To sustain the species we must bring opposites

together. To explain our existence we must make
sense of opposites and extremes and polarities. For
example, healers need illness to express their gift of
healing, and peacemakers need conflict to bring
forward their peacemaking medicine.

It is somewhere in the coming together of the
seeming opposites that creativity and abundance
live and prosper. As the continuum underlying
polarities, dualities, opposites, and paradox are
seen, the crossroads and thresholds are created
where healing occurs. On the bridge between
opposite shores we find connection, compromise,
creativity and *deep medicine.*

## Step Five

# Finding Our Place:
# Our Planetary Heritage

PEACE COMES WITHIN
THE SOULS OF MEN WHEN
THEY REALIZE THEIR ONENESS
WITH THE UNIVERSE.

*BLACK ELK*

*This we know. The Earth does not belong to man. Man belongs to Earth. This we know. All things are connected like the blood which unites all in one family. Will you teach your children what we have taught our children? That the Earth is our Mother? Whatever befalls the Earth befalls the sons of the Earth. Man did not weave the web of life, he is merely a strand in it. Whatever he does to the web, he does to himself.*

**– Chief Seattle**
Letter to U.S. President Franklin Pierce, 1854

Bearing witness to the contact points between science and the sacred, we are led to the relationship between humankind and Mother Earth. Scientific data and cultural wisdom have told us that we have an intimate relationship with Planet Earth, such that the health of the individual person is inseparable from that of the planet. In our fast-paced, urban and suburban twenty-first century lifestyles, we have lost sight of this reality. Rediscovering and reclaiming this relationship is the next step in practicing deep medicine.

### Perspective

Every generation of humans considers the time of their living as an age of challenge, filled with amazing developments. What has happened in the last one hundred years makes the previous one thousand or twenty thousand years look like dormancy. One hundred years ago, transportation, communication, and ecological disaster meant riding the horse into town and stopping at the general store to talk about the creek overflowing its banks. Today, we telecommunicate with all corners of the globe, access the archives of human knowledge or destroy far reaches of the planet—all in seconds.

The magnitude and pace of human evolution, particularly in the realm of science and technology, need also to be evaluated as an existential crisis. We have people in space, genetic engineering, and the Internet. But we also have increasing disparity between haves and have-nots, unprecedented violence, and more attention and money paid to state prisons than to public education. There is the real possibility of individual and planetary illness owing to population explosion, accompanying toxic wastes, and climate crisis.

There seems to be a disparity between our rapidly growing knowledge base and expanding technologic skills and our moral and ethical development.

Long before the advent of contemporary scientific thinking, many land and water-based indigenous peoples lived in harmony with their environment. Our modern way of life and rapidly increasing numbers have robbed us of the kind of relationships our forebears had with their habitats. How many of us have mapped the terrain where we live, understand the water runoff of our local watershed, or know the local flora and fauna? Who among us has a concept of the food chain in our area? How might we live differently if we were as fully in tune with our surroundings as Native American peoples, tribes of Africa, the herders of Tibet, and others who live close to the land and sea?

Recall the myths from divergent cultures chronicling the honorable, respectful, and compassionate relationship these people had with the Earth. Consider Chief Seattle's quote, which heads Step Five. The pace and pattern of our lives and the status of our health would improve by honoring our connection to the billions of years of creative metamorphosis that have formed our universe, solar system, and planet. I am not suggesting a return to cave and candle, but an adjustment in perspective that allows our relatedness to the planet to be fully seen, expressed, and valued.

From DDT-poisoned birds, to radioactive milk, to mercury in fish, we have become familiar with a host of environment-related diseases and toxicities affecting humans and other species.

James Lovelock, in his book *The Ages of Gaia: A Biography of Our Living Earth*, credits Dr. James Hutton, cited in Step Three's discussion of the ecologic metaphor, with suggesting that healthcare that dealt only with the health of one species (i.e., human health) would be inadequate. A shift to a broader perspective is necessary.

### Planetary Health

Daily, we are faced with examples of planetary degradation that directly impact health: air pollution, ozone depletion, global warming, water contamination, topsoil erosion, rainforest destruction, inter-species infections, human overpopulation, waste disposal, and threat of nuclear disaster. The tabulation, though incomplete, reads like the table of contents of a medical book describing the various states of human disease. Congenital deformities, infections and infestations, degenerative changes, fluid and electrolyte imbalances, nutritional deficiencies, respiratory distress, psychological illnesses, and cancers plague our bodies along with the maladies that plague our environment.

Our intimate relationship with the Earth is emphasized not only by our shared maladies but by significant physiological commonalities. The proportion of water in our bodies is about the same as that of the earth's surface. The concentration of salt in the oceans is similar to that in human blood. The proportion of oxygen in the atmosphere allows aerobic reactions without uncontrollable combustion. The universe is expanding fast enough so that the force of gravity does not pull all back together, but slowly enough so that we do not fly off unrestrained into distant space.

These and other microscopic and macroscopic relationships between humans and the natural world remind us of our planetary heritage: we are of the planet, not just on it. From this vantage point we can see the Earth as a whole—like the now familiar blue-green image from space—and appreciate our planet as the living organism that it is.

The challenge to maintain the delicate life-sustaining proportions and balances is truly the healthcare issue of the times. Our precious planet provides the only potable water, fertile topsoil and oxygen-containing atmosphere for a trillion miles or more. There is not a backup planet!

As I became aware of these exquisite biologic and chemical, mathematic and physics-based relationships, the elegance of the whole interplay moved me deeply. I was compelled as a physician to bring an appreciation of the value and power of these relationships forward in the medical setting. Understanding and honoring these delicate environmental balances makes each of us official "Physicians to the Earth." Keepers of balance, restorers of equilibrium, vital elements in the equation. It was an idealistic desire to create the first "Department of Planetary Medicine" at a major medical center that contributed to the beginnings of what is now the Institute for Health & Healing in San Francisco.

Brian Swimme and Father Thomas Berry in their book *The Universe Story* suggest that humans are literally the consciousness, the awareness of the planet. We are an integral part of the planet. When we care about what is happening to the Earth, the Earth is caring for itself. The next time some troublesome skeptic asks you if the Earth really cares about _____ (fill in the blank with, for example, "using up the oil," "destroying the rainforests," "exterminating species"), you can legitimately answer, "Yes!" If we care, the Earth cares.

### Where Are We?

The planetary perspective is an important element of deep healing and healthy choosing. Looking at the planet this way usually requires a shift in perspective. Brian Swimme has said that if we really knew where we were we would know how to behave. Harry Golden, in *Only in America*, writes about where we are, from an astronomer's view of the cosmos.

Explaining why he never bawls out a waitress in a restaurant for taking too long to bring dinner:

> "There are at least four billion suns in the Milky Way, which is only one galaxy. Many of these suns are thousands of times larger than our own, and vast millions of them have whole planetary systems.... Our own sun and its planets, which include this earth, are on the edge of...space...so unbelievably vast that if we reduced the suns and the planets in correct mathematical proportions with relation to the distances between them, each sun would be a speck of dust, two, three, and four thousand miles away from its nearest

neighbor. And mind you, this is only the
Milky Way—our own small corner—our own
galaxy. How many galaxies are there?
Billions."

## Big Rocks

Appreciating our place in the cosmic scheme of
things can help us make sound health-generating
decisions. With the perspective to see our planetary
impact, we have greater awareness of what impacts
us individually.

My friend, Sandra Hobson, shared with me the
following anecdote about the importance of seeing
things in proper perspective:

> "One day an expert in time management was
> speaking to a group of business students and,
> to drive home a point, used an illustration
> those students will never forget. As he stood
> in front of the group of high-powered
> achievers he said, 'Okay, time for a quiz.'
>
> He pulled out a one-gallon, wide-mouthed
> Mason jar and set it on the table in front of
> him. He produced about a dozen fist-sized
> rocks and carefully placed them, one at a
> time, in the jar.
>
> When the jar was filled to the top and no
> more rocks would fit inside, he asked, 'Is this
> jar full?'
>
> When everyone in the class said yes, he said,
> 'Really?' He reached under the table and
> pulled out a bucket of gravel.

Then he dumped some gravel in and shook the jar, which caused pieces of gravel to work down into the space between the big rocks. Then he asked the group once more, 'Is this jar full?'

By this time, the class was on to him. 'Probably not,' one of them answered. 'Good!' he replied. He reached under the table and brought out a bucket of sand. He started dumping the sand in the jar and it went into all of the spaces left between the rocks and the gravel. Once more he asked the question, 'Is this jar full?' and the class shouted, 'No!' Next he brought out a pitcher of water. Once again he poured it in until the jar was filled to the brim. Then he looked at the class and asked, 'What is the point of this illustration?'

One eager beaver raised his hand and said, 'The point is, no matter how full your schedule is, if you try really hard you can always fit some more things into it!'

'No,' the speaker replied, 'That's not the point. The truth this illustration teaches us is that if you don't put the big rocks in first, you'll never get them in at all!'"

What are the big rocks in your life? Your children, your loved ones, your education, your dreams, a worthy cause, teaching or mentoring others, doing things you love, time for yourself, your health, your significant other, riding your Harley Davidson? Remember to put those BIG ROCKS in first or you'll never get them in at all.

If you sweat only the small stuff (the gravel and the sand), you'll fill your life with the little things that aren't essential. Then you'll never have the real quality time you need to spend on the big, important things. So, with your planetary perspective, ask yourself this question: *"What are the big rocks in my life?"* Put those in your jar first.

## What Time Is It?

From a planetary perspective time is measured in epochs and eras. In a spiritual sense time is eternal. To paraphrase the sacred Hindu text the *Bhagavad-Gita*: Having been you always were and always will be. From the vantage point of our daily lives, time is measured in minutes, hours, days, and years. From a scientific view, time is relative. However we conceive of time, our individual existence is transient. All aspects of creation demonstrate a dynamic impermanence. This provides an element of unpredictability and uncertainty to our lives.

This impermanence is one of the strong arguments for aware, awake, mindful living in the present moment. We never really know which moment will be our last—when loss, tragedy, or good fortune will appear or disappear. We balance every breath in with a breath out.

We simultaneously and repeatedly give and receive, hold onto and let go, add the new and discard the used, seek and lose, grow and decay, get injured and heal, hurt and forgive. It is the nature of our existence over time to grow and change. Even as we experience the joy of growing children, they are leaving us. Living fully now is the best insurance against the tragedy of the unlived life.

The planetary perspective in time and space gives us reason to make the most of our conscious moments, in all the domains of our lives.

Finding our place in the family of things and relating in a way that frames our belonging to the planet properly is part of practicing deep medicine. It is said that the practice of relationship is all one needs for their spiritual journey. Certainly appreciating and living the differences among falling in love (egoistic, romantic, fantasy), being in love (commitment, loyalty, shared goals) and staying in love (growth, change, partnership) provide fertile ground for character development, learning awareness, and gaining in consciousness. To love requires curiosity and understanding, communication and creativity, honor and respect. These characteristics define our relationship with our planet—our Mother Earth—as well. Nothing short of a loving relationship will allow us a healing partnership with our planet.

This, too, is part of practicing deep medicine.

*See the world as yourself.*

*Have faith in the way things are.*

*Love the world as yourself;*

*Then you can care for all things.*

**– Lao Tzu**
Tao Te Ching

⌘     **Exercise for Step Five:**     ⌘
**Personal Health and Planetary Healing**

- Reflect on your own personal relationship with the planet. (*Hint:* It's not called Mother Earth for nothing.)
- Where did your lunch come from (and I don't mean Dave's Deli)? Where will it go? (*Hint:* Start with dirt, finish with...)
- When you say "throw it away"—Where is away?
- Why was (is) the sun worshipped?
- Consider the man-made aspects of:
  - Drought and famine in Africa
  - Global warming
  - Respiratory disease in Los Angeles
  - Chernobyl in the former U.S.S.R.
- Consider the health implications of:
  - Mass transit
  - Recycling
  - Organic farming
  - Disposables
- Was (Is) Chief Seattle correct? (see his quote at the beginning of Step Five)
- Consider the following relational sequences in the context of the evolutionary history of the planet:
  - *Subatomic particles→ molecules→ cells→ tissues→ organs→ systems→ organisms*
  - *Elements→ matter→ life→ mind→ consciousness*
  - *Individual→ family→ tribe→ city→ state→ nation→ humankind*
- Where are you and what time is it? Is it the right place and the right time? If not, what do you have to do to make it so?

## Step Six

---

# Up Close and Personal:
# Your Story

*As is the human body, so is the cosmic body.*
*As is the human mind, so is the cosmic mind.*
*As is the microcosm, so is the macrocosm.*
*As is the atom, so is the universe.*

**– The Upanishads**
The Little Zen Companion

*Know thyself.*

**– Socrates**

In 1983 I visited India for the first time. There I had the privilege of working at the Aravind Eye Hospital in Madurai, in the state of Tamil Nadu. The hospital is the result of the visionary work of Dr. G. Venkataswamy.

After his retirement in 1976 as the chair of the Department of Ophthalmology at the nearby medical school, he was moved by a desire to serve his community with a higher standard of ophthalmic care, regardless of one's capacity to pay or caste. Dr. V, as he is lovingly called, opened a small eye hospital in a converted house with two operating rooms and twelve beds.

From this humble beginning, with the help of his dedicated family, the organization has grown to become the world's largest eye care system. Today they care for more than 1.25 million patients and perform over 250,000 surgeries per year at five hospitals. What makes this even more remarkable is that approximately two-thirds of the cases are done on the "free hospital" service. Each of the patients who is able to pay supports two who cannot. The work is of the highest quality, done to international standards, and is accomplished with a balanced budget.

Where does the energy come from that allows the motivated people who run these productive hospitals to serve with kindness and integrity? Where do the meaning and rewards come from for a staff frequently required to entertain foreign visitors, paid modest salaries, and working long hours? How do they deal with unending patient and teaching responsibilities and still demonstrate productivity five times the average ophthalmic surgeon in India? It is clear in visiting one of the

Aravind Eye Hospitals that a sense of sacred purpose pervades the medical setting. Days begin quietly in the hospital's small meditation room.

Underlying the bustle of busy operating rooms (often with two or three surgeries occurring simultaneously) and the chaos of the crowded corridors, waiting rooms, and clinics is a reverence for every being. There is a deep powerful connection and nourishment from an unseen energy reservoir— a spirit of service. Here is a place where science and soul are yoked. Here is a model that demonstrates a collaborative relationship between scientific expertise and spiritual richness—between the visible and invisible.

## The Power of Purpose

One evening during that first trip to India, my wife Susy left the powerful words of the Indian poet Tagore on my pillow:

> *I slept and dreamt that life was joy,*
> *I awoke and found that life was service,*
> *I served and behold, service was joy.*

Dr. V, a physically slight man with fingers gnarled from arthritis and a burning passion to fight the fight against needless blindness, personifies this poem. Dr. V is a healer of giant proportion and a surgeon who lives fully in the worlds of science and spirit. The purpose of his life and the meaning of his existence are clearly evident in his work, relationships, and vitality. His life's work is to eradicate needless blindness. He has addressed the work of healing with a passion and authenticity evident to all who encounter him. He has a coherence with his truth and purpose that is nourished by his deep spirituality. He is a follower of Gandhi and disciple of Indian sage Sri Aurobindo, who was a contemporary of Gandhi and a freedom fighter for India's independence.

Dr. V begins his day with a silent meditation—a "talk with God"—and a reading from Sri Aurobindo's writings. Through his meditation he seeks to be a better instrument of the Divine will. He strives to be able to overcome anger, jealousy, and egotism and to find a way to show compassion to each person he encounters. Dr. V has overcome many obstacles in achieving the volume, quality, and efficiency in medical and surgical care that the Aravind Eye Care System displays. But his accomplishments in medicine must be seen in the context of the striking disability that he had to overcome and transcend. For the fingers of this superb surgeon, this innovator of high productivity surgical care for the common man of India, are twisted and deformed and stiff from severe arthritis that struck him while he was a young man in medical training. Yet he himself has done more than 100,000 eye surgeries.

Being in Dr. V's presence one cannot but feel his integrity, truth, authenticity and his connection with the unseen world. Yet he is humble, quiet, and shuns attention. His life and work seamlessly integrate deeply held spiritual beliefs and practices and compassionate service in the secular, contemporary world.

Dr. V says that it is not out of sympathy that you want to help others but out of the realization that "…you are identified with whom or for whom you work in a way that the sufferer is a part of you. … When we grow in spiritual consciousness, we identify ourselves with all that is in the world, and there is no exploitation. It is ourselves we are helping. It is ourselves we are healing." (*Illuminated Spirit* by Govindappa Venkataswamy.)

Meeting Dr. V and the wonderful members of his family and team—who as surgeons, administrators, contractors, scientists, writers, filmmakers, and bearers of goodwill move the work of eradicating needless blindness forward—has been a transformative experience for me.

I went to India the first time as a young, well-trained surgeon full of myself and the potential to help those doing ophthalmic surgery in the developing world. I came home humbled by the volume and quality of the work being done, deeply moved by the compassion demonstrated, inspired by the generosity of spirit I saw, and changed by the joy that emanated from these deeply committed, disciplined, hard-working people. Susy and I were accepted with a grace and kindness that opened my mind, my heart, and my world to the power of trust in the Divine, and to the possibility that integrity and strength of purpose could not only survive but thrive in the contemporary world. To this day, I continue to be grateful to Susy and Marcia and Dr. David Vastine, who together planned and organized our first trip to India. I may have left a few lessons in surgical technique in India, but I returned home with life lessons. It is said that once you visit India you will never be the same, and for me it is true.

Experiencing the practice of medicine under Dr. V's leadership in India changed my life forever in a way imaged beautifully by Juan Ramón Jiménez:

*My boat struck something deep.*
*Nothing happened. Waves, water, silence.*
*Nothing happened?*
*Or perhaps everything happened.*
*And I am sitting in the middle of my new life.*

## Making the Planetary Personal

Our stories individualize the big picture and make the planetary personal. We are each a minute but essential player in the unfolding drama of earthly existence. Each of us brings unique baggage for the journey.

The work of two lifelong students of Rudolf Steiner is illustrative. George and Gisela O'Neil delineate the story of human life into three main phases:

1. *Birth to about twenty years*—bodily maturity is accomplished;
2. *Middle years to about forty years*—emotional and psychological stability occurs;
3. *Thereafter*—individual and spiritual maturity may follow.

The issues and demands are different at each stage of the human story. Successful behavior at one age will not work at another time. Inadequate preparation during an early phase may leave us unready for the next. The demands of an infant will not be met with what the preschooler needs. An adolescent's appropriate behavior will not propel the young career person forward.

The deep medicine we seek can be found within our biology and chronology, as well as in our progress on our spiritual path. This is an inner and outer, ongoing revisioning and revitalizing of our state of being—not just of our state of doing! Each stage builds on the previous one. All are important as we evolve in healthy ways.

Our present-day issues—physical, mental, emotional, and spiritual—are related to underlying needs that are affected by our circumstances—from genetic to environmental. In *Why People Don't Heal and How They Can*, Carolyn Myss explains that our biology and biography are inseparable.

Our reaction to any particular stimulus will be dictated by our individual story. Our response will determine the influence of any particular stimulus on our health. Of course this response will come within the context of our personal health ecology and include the social, cultural, economic, and geopolitical circumstances in which we live.

Try as we might to create generalizations about what makes us healthy or ill or how any particularly defined group or type will act, our responses are uncertain, our futures beyond forecasting. In the final analysis, we are predictable only to a point. We each have our own special wisdom and gifts—our own medicine—to bring forward.

Everyone's story is to be heard in an openhearted, full, present way. But our stories do not need to be epic or classic, neither melodrama, soap opera, nor lab report. What is told needs to be honest, simple, and authentically our own. The importance of our story can be seen in the following age-old tale. Sometimes what we see as defects, flaws, or difficulties in ourselves bear unexpected fruit, lead us on a productive new path, or stimulate the growth of something or someone else.

## The Cracked Pot Story

There is a familiar fable about a water bearer in India who had two large pots. A pot hung on each end of a pole that he carried across his neck. One of the pots had a crack in it, and while the other pot was perfect and always delivered a full portion of water at the end of the long walk from the stream to the master's house, the cracked pot arrived only half full. For a full two years this went on daily, with the bearer delivering only one and a half pots full of water to his master's house. Of course, the perfect pot was proud of its accomplishments, perfect to the end for which it was made.

But the poor cracked pot was ashamed of its own imperfection, and miserable that it was able to accomplish only half of what it had been made to do.

After two years of what it perceived to be a bitter failure, it spoke to the water bearer one day by the stream. "I am ashamed of myself, and I want to apologize to you." "Why?" asked the bearer, "What are you ashamed of?"

"I have been able, for these past two years, to deliver only half of my load because this crack in my side causes water to leak out all the way back to your master's house. Because of my flaws, you have to do all of this work, and you don't get full value from your efforts," the pot said.

The water bearer listened to the old cracked pot, and in his compassion he said, "As we return to the master's house, I would like you to notice the beautiful flowers along the path." Indeed, as they went up the hill, the old cracked pot took notice of the sun warming the beautiful wild flowers on the side of the path, and this cheered it some. But at the end of the trail, it still felt bad because it had leaked out half its load, and so again, it apologized to the bearer for its failure.

The bearer said to the pot, "Did you notice that there were flowers only on your side of the path, but not on the other pot's side? That's because I have always known about your flaw, and I took advantage of it. I planted flower seeds on your side of the path, and every day while we walked back from the stream, you have watered them. For two years I have been able to pick these beautiful flowers to decorate my master's table. Without you being just the way you are, he would not have this beauty to grace his house."

Moral of the story: Each of us has our own unique flaws. We are all "cracked pots." So do not be afraid of your flaws. Acknowledge them, and you, too, can create much beauty in life.

## Everybody Counts: Your Story

Your story is important. Each of us is unique and has our story. Learning of your ancestral roots—cultural, spiritual, and familial—links you to your heritage and helps define who you are. Knowing where you came from is a part of self-knowledge. Knowing yourself is essential to authentically telling your story. It is through telling our story that we come to be known by others.

It is by listening to the stories of others that we become connected to them. It is through connection and relationship that trust builds and deep healing can take place. With deep healing, personal transformation occurs. It is through personal transformation that lasting social change occurs.

My story and my Jewish roots link me directly to an ancient spiritual tradition. My experience with oppression and slavery is not merely a Biblical tale but literally genetic. My understanding of genocide and annihilation is not only about pioneers emigrating to America for a new life and impacting the lives of native peoples in the process. The reality of attempted genocide lives in my story through my unknown relatives who were stripped of all they had, displaced, or killed during the Holocaust of WWII. I am connected through my story with the descendants of African-American slaves, with the Native peoples who have seen their traditions and lands confiscated and degraded, and with Asian, Latin, and other immigrants who are exploited and disrespected because of their differentness or our fears of scarcity, or in the name of economics.

In the end, relating to individuals at the level of their stories and traditions reveals connections that are deeply healing. These connections are deeper than a sense of service or fairness or compassion. These connections inform our caring for ourselves and others.

Our connections can be traced back beyond the judgments and fears that fuel our dismissal and disregard of that which we don't identify with or understand. We then encounter and appreciate a braiding of our different strands as elemental and powerful as our strands of DNA.

Further evolution of the human consciousness individually and collectively will be required for us to move beyond the boundaries of tribal warfare and personal prejudices. We can forward that evolution through our own personal exploration and healing work. Part of that work rests in a search of our traditional roots and a tracking of the true basis of our opinions and positions. Part of that healing work involves an investigation of what ignites us, pushes our buttons, and causes us to react, shut down, collapse, or leave. Tracing our roots, telling our story, and hearing the stories of others are actions that lead to healing for the teller and the listener. This is deep medicine. My power to heal and effect change lies in my good fortune of privilege and position and my passion to express and share my gifts and talents in a way that goes beyond myself and immediate family. But I can heal also because of the discovery of my personal story. This story has allowed me entry into the collective conversation of how together we can be forces of healing (wholeness) rather than of separation or disease.

So, flaws and all, we need to show up fully to the party. Being fully present *is* a present—our gift to every encounter, situation, and relationship in which we are all involved.

## Stories to Keep, Stories to Change

Stories can and often need to change. We have the power to change our stories, e.g., from a grievance story where we are the victim to a transformative story where we are the shape shifter or agent of change.

Stories can not only be transformed, they transform. Stories can shift, and heal, our reality. We each have struggles, opinions, points of view, blind spots. We each demonstrate repeated behavior patterns, habits, conditioned responses to many situations. How we describe a situation, in and of itself, contributes to defining the situation and how we respond to it. We each live with stories. Stories we are told. Stories we tell. These stories—how we describe ourselves to others, and how we interpret the stories of others—can be constructive or destructive, health creating or health negating.

Storytelling, like our talk of willingness to change or resistance to change, can strengthen, inspire, move us to action or can undermine, stifle, and obstruct our growth. We must always be vigilant with what we are telling others and what we are telling ourselves. Our "self-talk" can build us up or tear us down. We need our stories to be such that we want them to happen. We need to create constructive possibilities for ourselves with our self-talk—not tales that feed our fears and doubts, or foster resentments and conflicts. As our stories change so will our outlook and our responses to ourselves and others.

I have stories in my life that have required re-writing—or at least reinterpretation—as times change, circumstances change, and even people change. When the Institute for Health & Healing and its precursor programs were evolving at the California Pacific Medical Center in San Francisco, I often saw myself as the rebel or freedom fighter: a marginalized radical bringing forward principles and practices that the entrenched medical hierarchy didn't want to hear or see. I had pushback to overcome, obstacles to circumnavigate, walls to climb, and barriers to break down. It felt like a struggle, a battle. I often spoke of the resistance I was encountering, how people didn't get it, and how little support I was getting.

Now this was a story I really believed. Well, I believed it as long as I could. But eventually the facts flew in the face of my belief. We actually received our initial start-up grant from the Medical Center. The Medical Center's Foundation added us to their organization chart so we had a home and they raised thousands of dollars for us. Space and overhead support as well as administrative salaries were provided by the Medical Center. Not long after I stopped doing surgery so I could become the full-time Medical Director of the Institute, I was invited onto the Medical Center's Senior Management Team. Didn't it seem about time to change the story?

Could I still pretend to be a rebel with a cause when anyone objectively looking at what was going on would appropriately conclude that we were a vital, valued part of the Medical Center's vision and mission? What part of me was unable to trust the creative unfolding that was occurring? What kind of arrogance did this mistrust belie in me? Of course I was passionate about my dream of holistic medicine being a part of contemporary medical practice at major, established medical centers. That didn't mean that I could expect to control every twist and turn of this emerging.

Many questions such as these were raised in me and required self-reflection and tracking. What was my capacity to trust? My need to control? My fears of failure? My self-worth, sufficiency, and the level of commitment to my dream all begged for attention. This level of self-searching, self-diagnosis, with or without expert guidance, is necessary for each of us. No self-help program—absent the deep, often painful, inner work—will succeed in a sustainable way. This kind of search and discovery mission is self-empowering. It will help us overcome those aspects of our experience that have misinformed us.

Self-inquiry will help us find the personal presence and authenticity to minimize the brainwashing that advertised consumerism, political spin, parochial media, and so-called opinion makers deliver to us. There is great freedom and hope available in a clear viewing of ourselves and a setting of expectations that are not caged by self-limiting story.

Making the transition to a new story is like re-making your life. It need not be major surgery. Sometimes it is a subtle or gentle realignment.

Several years ago, Susy and I had the good fortune to visit Ireland on retreat with Celtic poet, theologian, and philosopher John O'Donohue. One day, as we hiked the evocative landscape near John's boyhood home, I was struggling with an old story that I considered to be of cultural origin. It concerned the belief I held that if things were going well, they were bound to turn bad. I was moved to ask John about this, appreciating that the Irish people had experienced much hardship and misery in their history. I was wondering if he harbored a similar belief. He acknowledged the widespread acceptance of my version of the story which is fear-based and even in times of joy can lead to worry and concern—because surely things are going to turn bad any moment. He suggested a revision to the story. His version was that things are going so well— it is so wonderful—it is too good to be true. In this version we are joyful, uplifted, and grateful for the goodness, not worrying about the transient nature of our well-being. A subtle change can make a big difference. It is not necessarily the really big things we need to change, but just some of the little insignificant things.

Sometimes those who seem disruptive, or that which appears to be an obstacle, can be a catalyst to learning. Sometimes detours actually lead to shortcuts and gains—not lost time or ground.

### "Shake It Off—Step Up"

The farmer and the old mule...

"One unfortunate day, the old mule fell into the farmer's dry well. The farmer heard the mule's piteous braying and noted an unusual amount of distress in the tenor of his cries. The farmer discovered his mule's sad plight, and became quite upset. Tears came to his eyes and he ached in his heart. He loved all his animals, especially his old mule.

After carefully assessing the situation, the farmer realized the well was a safety hazard. He became angry with himself for not closing off the well and preventing such an accident. Sadly, he could think of no way to extricate his beloved mule from the depths of the well.

The farmer called his neighbors together and told what had happened. He then enlisted them to help haul dirt to fill up the dry well, and, at the same time, put his old mule out of misery.

Initially, the old mule became more hysterical. The dirt being thrown upon his back made him that much more upset. But, as the farmer and his neighbors continued shoveling and the dirt hit his back, he would shake off the dirt and take a step up. This he did, blow after blow.

*'Shake it off... Step up.'*

*'Shake it off... Step up.'*

*'Shake it off... Step up.'*

He repeated the above mantra to encourage himself.

No matter how painful the blows from the dirt, or how distressing the situation seemed, the old mule fought panic and kept right on shaking the dirt off, and stepping up, ever higher and higher.

It wasn't long before the old mule, battered and exhausted, stepped triumphantly over the wall of the well."

**– Author Unknown**
retrieved from *www.woohoo.net*

So listen to stories with care—especially those that you tell yourself over and over as reasons why you can't, won't or don't, shouldn't or should. What stories do you tell yourself that keep you from what you desire? That you don't have time, can't afford it, or will do it next time, next year? Listen to these recurring excuses, rationalizations, explanations, or stories. *Listen* carefully to your language and the terms you choose to describe yourself and others. Then *track* their source and be prepared to change the story!

## Stories Heal

From our sense of connectedness with the planet and to others, to a concept of self, to healing stories and stories to change, we can focus further on our individual stories and their influence on our well-being. Here we see how the hand we are dealt—our genetic makeup, our family of origin, our upbringing—affects our health.

While I was a visiting professor at a nearby university medical center, I was introduced to a patient whose case illustrates how we can be blind to our own story and its influence on our medical status. This patient was a young, generally healthy woman suffering from a severe inflammatory condition around one of her eyes.

Her complaints included pain and difficulty with vision. Her findings included redness, swelling, and reduced movement of the eye. She had been extensively questioned and evaluated by the physicians who were responsible for her care. My time with her was short, and my review of the information available showed that the doctors had evaluated her extensively only to emerge with essentially normal findings other than those related to her red eye. Lacking any definite cause such as infection, cancer, or injury to explain her problem, I began to question her further. I asked, "Is there anything going on in your life that you might relate to the onset or progression of your illness?" She thought a moment and said that nothing unusual was happening.

I probed her ideation about the future, noting that she was accompanied by a young child and a middle-aged man. "Is there anything you consider stressful happening in your life?" As I asked the question, I explained that stress can contribute to many illnesses.

"No, everything is going all right. In fact, I was recently married!" she said. "Congratulations! When was the wedding in relation to the onset of the eye problem?" I inquired. She explained that the problem came up before the wedding. However, she had been going through a divorce at the time (which had been contentious, with its finality in question right up to the date of her recent wedding). I nodded, and before I could ask anything further she reported that there was some further pressure since she had lost her job, her son had serious dental problems that they couldn't afford to treat, and her mother was hospitalized for a heart problem. She said she was terribly concerned and couldn't see their futures clearly. Her presenting medical signs and symptoms mirrored the circumstances of her life. Her treatment plan could then expand to deal with more than her physical findings.

When we face our individuality in the context of our relatedness to what has come before us and what surrounds us, we contribute to our wellness. What we do to understand our guiding principles and values contributes to our well-being. The immune system is challenged by our life's events. Recall that the most common time for students to get sick is during final exams; the most common time for heart attacks in men is Monday morning. Psychosocial support can contribute to survival in cancer patients; married men live longer than unmarried men.

## The Problem and the Solution
## Are Often in the Mirror

No one can know another as well as we know ourselves. Through our self-knowledge, we can be active healers of ourselves. Although we can, and often should, seek help from others (doctors, friends, teachers, clergy, and other healers), we also must use our self-knowledge to identify patterns that are either good for us or limit us. Then we must make choices. Decide what to do and what not to do, when to push forward, when to hold back.

Each individual story begins with an inherited genetic map and the circumstances that we are born into. We all have tales of the trials, tribulations, and treasures of our upbringing and family of origin. Some of what we are and will be has been cast and is beyond our influence. Nonetheless, a good bit of our story can be influenced. How we respond to what has happened to us is in large part under our jurisdiction. How we see and engage our present set of circumstances, and prepare for and dream the future, are also within our own purview.

No physician would argue with the importance of our genetic makeup and inherited traits and tendencies as contributors to our health and illness. Neither would any healer argue with the powerful impact our life choices, lifestyles, thoughts, emotions, attitudes, and behaviors have on our health.

Outside the small incidence of inherited full-blown disease states, the power of contemporary medicine and surgery notwithstanding, our lifestyle choices are likely the single most important potentially manageable component in the delicate balance that brings about health and healing. In making these choices, we are creating and living our story and practicing deep medicine.

⌘          **Exercise for Step Six:**          ⌘
**That's My Story, What's Yours?**

Decisions require personal knowledge of what fills
us and what depletes us. It is necessary that we set
and pursue priorities with intention and honesty. In
so doing, answer the following:
- Who am I? What am I seeking?
- What is motivating me to seek?
- Am "I" my physical body, my personality,
  my soul?
- Do I really stop at the limits of my skin?
- How far does my mind, consciousness reach?
- Where were my molecules, atoms before they
  were me?
- What of my ancestral roots? Reflect on the
  background of your name.
- Who were my parents
    - What were their hopes?
    - What were their fears?
    - What were their dreams?
    - What did they think, feel about and how
      did they deal with...

      | Work | Play |
      |------|------|
      | Health | Illness |
      | Conflict | Anger |

      ...and how do I?

Have you ever said or thought, "That makes
me sick!"
- Can you identify certain circumstances that
  literally make you sick?
- Can you identify behavior patterns that
  repeatedly lead you to those circumstances?
- Anything you could do to avoid those
  circumstances?

Reflect on your story. How does it fit with the "big picture" and your legacy?

- Why are you presently living where you are living?
- Honor your past. Consider doing a family tree.
- Envision your future. Create a visioning ritual.
- Write in a journal—a personal journal is a useful tool for self-expression and discovery, and a good place to record your answers to the *Deep Medicine* exercise questions.
- Invite someone to tell you their story and listen with your heart as well as your ears.

As presented in Angeles Arrien's *Four-Fold Way Newsletter*, Olympic runner Bill Mills offers "Eight Lies of Iktumi", the trickster or liar figure from the Lakota tradition, which can jeopardize happiness or set up obstacles in a person's life:

- If only I were rich, then I would be happy.
- If only I were famous, then I would be happy.
- If only I could find the right person to marry, then I would be happy.
- If only I had more friends, then I would be happy.
- If only I were more attractive, then I would be happy.
- If only I weren't physically handicapped in any way, then I would be happy.
- If only someone close to me hadn't died, then I would be happy.
- If only the world were a better place, then I would be happy.

None of these stories is true in relationship to our happiness and salvation. We obsessively strive at work and at home for as many of the eight illusions as we can. Once these goals are attained we are often stunned to find ourselves still without satisfaction, still without meaning, or still without happiness. According to Iktumi's ways, ceasing to strive allows us to become liberated from our own fear, false attachments and desires.

- Take time to reflect on which of the eight lies has driven your personal and professional expression in different areas of your life.
- Other questions about your circumstances and  present health status or symptoms:
    - Is there a message?
    - Is there an underlying truth?
    - Is there a payoff? What's in it for you?

For example:

- Is your chronic sore back related to the load you are presently carrying?
- Has a health condition or illness taught you something about yourself that you were denying, avoiding or unable to see—and thus led you to change your life?
- Do your symptoms gain you attention, sympathy, or an escape from an unsatisfactory situation?
- Can illness be more than an obstacle or a challenge?
- Can illness be a wake up call, activator, or opening?

About your stories:
- Is there a story to discard?
- Is there a story to change?
- Is there language to change?
- Is there a story to live?

Consider the following and how it relates to your thoughts, words, stories, and behavior:

*The thought manifests as the word;*

*The word manifests as the deed;*

*The deed develops into habit;*

*And habit hardens into character.*

*So watch the thought and its ways with care,*

*And let it spring from love*

*Born out of concern for all beings.*

**– Buddha**

## Step Seven

# From Aspiration to Action:
# Where the Rubber Hits the Road

MAKE OF
YOURSELF
A LIGHT.
*BUDDHA*

*If you want to change the world, first change yourself.
And when you are changed, truly changed,
everything around you will be changed.*

**– Sri Aurobindo** and **The Mother of Pondicherry**

*It is not the same to talk of bulls
as to be in the bullring.*

**– Spanish Proverb**

*You cannot solve a problem
with the same mentality that created it.*

**– Albert Einstein**

As we gain insight and perspective, we are challenged to act. Practical, sustainable actions move us along the healing path. In this chapter we plot a course of action. You create a customized "business plan" for your health and healing.

Through the first six Steps, we have established a *deep foundation* on which to base our health-creating choices and actions. It is a conceptual foundation that is compatible with objectivity and science. It sets a context that incorporates our beliefs, values, and faith. It is not a simple, unchanging recipe for better health. Instead, it's a data base that provides resources that can be used when and as needed.

As you move forward on your healing path, remember the basic lessons: be curious and willing to change; consider the whole—your connection to the earth and the greater good; be open to bridging what might appear to be contradictions; and tell your authentic story to yourself and others. Remember that your inner world needs as much attention as your outer world. Be generous with yourself—small steps are OK, they are sometimes mandatory. Your progress deserves acknowledgment and celebration. Emphasize what you did do, not what you didn't do!

## Deep Medicine

Now we are moving into the heart of the work. This requires you to be an intrepid explorer, an adventurer into an uncharted wilderness, populated by physical, mental, emotional, and spiritual inhabitants.

Whatever has brought you to this particular starting line—be it a desire to lose weight or prolong your productive lifetime, a bad habit, unfulfilling relationships, unsatisfying jobs, loss of direction, a search for meaning and purpose, a distressing illness, or curiosity—is less important than the realization that you are here at the starting gate. You must want to make a shift. You must deeply, fully want to change. If not, you would be doing something else now. Your motivation must come from within and it must be translated into witnessable action.

In order to be sustained, growth and change must be harnessed to a meaningful, truthful vision of who you are—a perspective that can continually rekindle your inner fire as you encounter obstacles. Flexibility, resourcefulness, creativity, commitment, and repeated, determined acts of will are all necessary on your path to health and healing. You will be required to discover and bring forward your true and beautiful gifts and talents. As you do this, it will be deeply healing medicine for you and those around you. The truth is always compelling to those who witness it.

Be assured that there will be resistance to your chosen path. Obstacles will present themselves. Detours will be necessary. They may appear as the family member you enable, the coworker cautioning you, difficulty getting out of bed for early morning exercise or meditation, the irresistible dessert menu, or the agonizingly slow response of your illness. You will lose energy, slip backward, stall out, want to quit, need a break, change teachers, seek second and third opinions, and feel fearful. Yet you will also find inspiration in unlikely places, marvel at the timeliness of that which is needed showing up when it does, the wisdom imparted by important strangers, and the coincidences that occur. Be sensitive to the "stage" that your change program seems to represent. Stay alert to your *change* or *resistance* thoughts and talk.

### Tips for the Trip

Imagine you're crossing a cold, rapidly flowing river encountered along your chosen route. As you look across to the other side, know that:

- Your exact destination may not be where you initially think it is.
- There is no perfect time or place to start.
- The route, and even the rules, are constantly changing.
- You will get cold, wet, and tired and stub your toes (or even lose them).
- You will lose and regain your balance many times.
- Sometimes the way that looks easier isn't.
- Sometimes the way that looks hardest isn't.
- Proper equipment, instruction, and preparation help progress.
- Small steps are OK.
- Backward or sideways steps are sometimes essential.
- Stopping and resting are important.

- Although focusing on the specific act at hand is imperative, it will be necessary to do more than one thing at a time as well as being aware of the big picture.
- Being afraid is not necessarily bad. Courage is not being unafraid, it is moving forward as you face your fear.
- In spite of your best intentions and efforts, circumstances will present themselves that disrupt your expectations, seeming to hinder your forward progress. However, what seems like a setback now may turn out to be a gift when seen in context over time.
- You must let go of the need for only rational, objective knowing and trust other ways of knowing (intuition, gut feeling, and inner voices).
- When you get to the other side, the tools, equipment and techniques you used to get there may no longer be useful. Be sure to let go of what you don't need. Today's building blocks may become tomorrow's burden.

### First Steps

Start where you are with what you have. Begin an experiment with yourself as the subject. In a scientific sense, it might be useful to put analysis aside for now, and simply observe. Pay attention to the results as you gather your personal data.

- Question yourself as to what resonates intellectually, emotionally and instinctively as the next step for you. What is your desired change? What do you really want and need? What exactly are you ready to try? This is an extremely important consideration as you approach change of any kind. Sometimes the attraction may be unconscious, but you are drawn to something or someone. How you respond depends on your *readiness* to change. What is truly important to you? Do you have enough confidence to undertake the "project" at this time?

- Explore the options by talking with friends, family and advisors.
- Sample what is out there through reading, lectures, the internet, workshops, and classes that seem to draw you for whatever reason. You want to start in the right place, at the right time, with the right tools.
- Practice tuning into and tracking your bodily responses. Did her remarks produce a queasy sensation in your stomach, raise your pulse rate and/or cause your heart to skip a beat? Did the encounter give you a headache, make you weary, or energize you? Pay attention to your internal responses. Note how your body feels, not just what you think about your experience. Trust your bodily responses. They are full of wisdom.
- Keep a journal—it will allow you to record what you learn in your experiments. A journal can serve to decompress emotions and provide a safe place to record dreams, feelings, thoughts and movement toward your goals. You can even plot your symptoms against a course of treatment you are receiving or keep a record of the results of your exercise program, or progress with your weight management plan.

Objective, measurable results are important markers of progress and serve as motivators on an ongoing basis. Your course will not be sustained by inspiration alone. Concrete results (weight loss, lowered blood pressure, reduced cholesterol levels) are rewards for your hard work. Your journal will help you monitor your progress. It will also be a place to record reactions, learnings, and observations. Was what occurred an interesting bit of additional information or a truly transformative experience? Each represents progress along the path, but of different nature and impact.

## Put On Your Own Oxygen Mask First

Regardless of your working destination and your chosen path, you must start by taking care of yourself. Although we often don't put our own needs first, this is mandatory. You cannot support your family or your work unless you yourself are as healthy as you can be—physically, mentally, emotionally, spiritually.

This requires that we do what the airlines remind us to do when a serious problem occurs during a flight. It is a familiar recitation: "Put on your own oxygen mask first, then help those around you." It is even necessary that you put on your own oxygen mask before you help your child, lest, from lack of air, you are unable to help those dearest to you. It is not being selfish to see to your own well-being first. It is an act of generosity to yourself and to those dependent on you. Don't feel guilty; don't feel greedy. It is only on a foundation of health—with wholeness and balance—that you can be of service to others.

We are all caregivers, and our care giving must start with ourselves. Charity really does begin at home. Share your energy in a sustainable way, not as a sacrifice, obligation, or responsibility. Share as a gift, as a relationship that serves the giver and the receiver. Does that mean you won't get tired? That you won't say yes to too many people? Of course not. But periodic losses of balance are temporary in the context of a life plan based on sound principles. Saying no will become easier as you recognize your limits and acknowledge your own health needs.

The essentials of self-care along your healing path depend on your state of health and life circumstances. Be creative and proactive as you modify these suggestions to suit your own needs. To sustain your self-care, you will likely need expert care as well. Initially, frequent follow-up with your doctors, healers, coaches, mentors, and guides will serve to sustain your practice toward your goals. As results are achieved, follow-up intervals can become longer. As your practices become better established, you will wean yourself from your support team and more and more sustain yourself. However, some type of relational support is essential. Never consider it a sign of weakness to check in with your support network as new circumstances arise.

## The Pillars of Self-Care

The endless bookshelves of self-help literature can be condensed into four universal categories of recommendations. These represent wisdom found in healing systems from multiple cultures, and create a solid foundation for self-care:

I.   Nutrition
II.  Physical Activity
III. Contemplation/Solitude
IV.  Relationship/Community

These pillars usually occur in various forms in different cultures as part of an inclusive system (e.g., Traditional Chinese Medicine, Ayurveda).

The pillars are not viewed in isolation, but are part of a multi-limbed approach. They include, among other things, guidelines regarding morals, ethics, and acceptable behaviors toward ancestors and elders. In the quick-fix-oriented West, we often see yoga as postures (asana) and neglect the well-defined recommendations and teachings that form the foundations for the practice. Then, what is a well-defined philosophy and comprehensive approach to life becomes reduced to an exercise class. Or the wisdom of generations of Traditional Chinese Medicine practitioners is whittled down to only the modality and practice of acupuncture, without consideration of the greater context in which the practice of acupuncture dwells.

So *wisdom practices* have a strong basis in the classic practices and empirical observations of traditional and indigenous cultures worldwide.

Their roots are deep, well tested through centuries of application and observation, and linked to moral and ethical principles as evidenced by the millennia-old writings in the *Yellow Emperor's Classic on Internal Medicine:*

"In the past, people practiced the Tao, the Way of Life. They understood the principle of balance, of yin and yang, as represented by the transformation of the energies of the universe. Thus they formulated ... exercises combining stretching, massaging, and breathing to promote energy flow, and meditation to help maintain and harmonize themselves with the universe.

They ate a balanced diet at regular times, arose and retired at regular hours, avoided overstressing their bodies and minds, and refrained from overindulgence of all kinds. They maintained well-being of body and mind; thus, it is not surprising that they lived over one hundred years.

These days, people have changed their way of life. They drink wine as though it were water, indulge excessively in destructive activities, drain their jing—the body's essence ... and deplete their qi [energy]. They do not know the secret of conserving their energy and vitality. Seeking emotional excitement and momentary pleasures, people disregard the natural rhythm and order of the universe. They fail to regulate their lifestyle and diet, and sleep improperly. So it is not surprising that they look old at fifty and die soon after."

Significant contemporary scientific evidence exists supporting the above wisdom from the *Yellow Emperor* and regarding the efficacy and value of these pillars of self-care.

Many superb references exist describing the theory and practices of various aspects of these core pillars. Particularly noteworthy are the similarities among recommendations from different modern traditions regarding various illness states or states of imbalance. For example, recommended diets for people with heart disease, diabetes, and arthritis have more similarities than differences.

## *I. Nutrition*

### Diet

It's obvious, and easily overlooked, that everything we eat becomes part of our bodies. There is no argument that we are what we eat. So watch what you eat—soon it will be you!

Regardless of your present diet of choice, notice the size of your portions. As a general rule of thumb, an appropriate portion is about the size of your fist. And calories still count! Contrary to popular belief, breaking cookies in half, eating ice cream out of the container, and eating standing up (or when nobody can see you) do not lower the calories present in foods. Low-fat and non-fat foods still have calories.

Balance your intake of carbohydrates, protein, and fat. The once popular high-carbohydrate, low-fat, low-protein approach to weight control may leave you hungry sooner, and may not be a healthy choice for you. The well known high protein, high fat diet option has staunch proponents but demonstrates high recidivism (i.e., weight lost is regained). Don't allow yourself to be drawn uncritically to the diet of the moment—it may not be a good one for you.

Seek fresh, locally grown, certified organic fruit and vegetables—and emphasize them in your daily menus. A colorful diet is generally a healthy diet. Emphasize whole grains and complex carbohydrates rather than simple sugars.

The terms "natural" and "organic" deserve special mention. Products with either of these designations cannot be used indiscriminately. Read labels carefully and be alert for added sugar, salt, and "bad" fats, such as trans fats or lard. In most states, the term *organic* can only be used on products when particular criteria are met, but the word *natural* is used more loosely. Mercury, hemlock, arsenic, cyanide, poison mushrooms, and radioactivity are all natural—and can be hazardous to your health. Allergic reactions, cross-reactions, or side effects can occur with organic products as well as with those not labeled organic.

Stay well hydrated. The old adage about drinking eight glasses of water each day may be excessive for many but the goal of adequate hydration is a good one. Water makes up a large percentage of your body's content and needs to be replenished. Drink before you are thirsty. If eight glasses of water per day cause you excessive trips to the bathroom, where you notice your urine is clear, you are likely drinking too much. Trust your thirst and seek to maintain a light yellow color to your urine. Neither pale, clear urine nor deeply colored, concentrated urine indicates a good balance point.

Don't forget your need for fiber. Opt for whole grains for the health of your digestive system and for better nutrition.

Use multiple protein sources, emphasizing soy, fish, low-fat poultry, and non-fat dairy products. Stay alert and current regarding reports of toxic contamination, e.g., mercury in fish. When possible, choose local seasonal organic foods.

Make olive oil your oil of choice. Omega-3 fatty acids—found in oily fish, such as salmon and sardines, as well as in canola, flaxseed, walnut, and to a lesser degree in soy oils—are good for reducing potential cardiac risk factors.

Garlic and ginger are tasty, beneficial ingredients. Garlic is a tonic for the cardiovascular system, reducing cholesterol and triglyceride levels, platelet aggregation (clumping), and blood pressure. It also fortifies the immune system and has antibacterial and antifungal effects. Ginger is good for the digestive system and also has anti-inflammatory properties, which reduce aches and pains. Tumeric is another popular, valued seasoning.

Small quantities of alcohol are acceptable. Remember, however, that alcohol has a high calorie content and little nutritive or medicinal value—the antioxidants of red wine notwithstanding.

Minimize your consumption of caffeine.

Minimize your consumption of sweets—while they taste good and may seem a treat, usually they are empty calories without significant nutrients. Avoid foods and beverages with added sugar and high fructose corn syrup.

Keep in mind that how you eat may be as important as what you eat. Prepare your food with respect. Turn off the television, light a candle, say grace, and eat slowly. Stop before you are full.

The Ayurveda system of health emphasizes individual constitution types in its approach to nutrition and health and weight management. An individualized approach of this type may be extremely valuable when other programs more familiar to Western readers have proved unsuccessful or are unappealing.

Useful resources on nutrition and diet include *The Omega Diet* by Artemis P. Simopoulos, M.D., and Jo Robinson; *Eat More, Weigh Less* by Dr. Dean Ornish; *The Zone* by Barry Sears and Bill Lawren; *The Soul of Food* by Deborah Kesten; and *Inner Beauty* by Reenita Malhotra. For more

complete information, see the Readings and
References appendix.

## Supplements

Vitamin and mineral supplements are valuable as
part of a daily health program, but they are
supplements, not substitutes. Although vitamins
derived from your diet are almost always more
beneficial than a pill, commercially available
supplements are useful additions to a health-
creating diet.

Be sure to include antioxidants in your
supplements—vitamin A (beta carotene), vitamins C
and E, and selenium. They help to reduce
breakdown at a cellular level and may aid resistance
to disease and support longevity. Vitamin E dosage
should be kept below 400 I.U. per day according to
recent data.

A daily low-dose aspirin may be a valuable
addition because of its cardiovascular protection
and anti-inflammatory effects. Be sure your doctors,
especially your surgeon, know you are using aspirin
because it prolongs bleeding and inhibits clot
formation (as do high doses of vitamin E and ginkgo
biloba).

Minerals like iron, potassium, chromium,
calcium, magnesium, and zinc may be worth using.
Remember that different circumstances necessitate
different recommendations. For example, iron
supplementation is not generally recommended for
older men, but is for menstruating women.

At a resource library, health food store, on the
Internet, or through your favorite practitioner, learn
more about other supplements and products that
might be useful additions to your wellness program.

Some examples are:
- Echinacea and goldenseal root for upper respiratory illness
- St. John's Wort taken orally for mild depression, and used topically in oil to relieve skin irritation
- *Arnica montana* for injuries, swelling, and bruises
- Ginseng as a general tonic
- Ginkgo for circulation and mental alertness
- Aloe vera for burns, dermatitis, and dry skin
- Chamomile as a tea or bath for its sedative properties
- Glucosamine sulfate and chondroitin sulfate for arthritis and joint problems

Recommendations regarding supplements and their dosages change frequently, as new information becomes available. Alpha-lipoic acid, L-acetyl carnitine, Vitamin D, and $CoQ_{10}$ are receiving considerable attention, and new discoveries appear regularly. So avoid the temptation to lock into a particular protocol. Keep your knowledge base current. Consider subscribing to a wellness newsletter from a reputable source such as the University of California School of Public Health, Consumer Reports, the Mayo Clinic, the Johns Hopkins School of Medicine, or Dr. Andrew Weil.

Good references regarding diet and supplements and general well-being include *Optimal Wellness* by Ralph Golan, M.D.; *Encyclopedia of Natural Medicine* by Michael Murray, ND, and Joseph Pizzorno, ND; *Nutritional Healing* by James and Phyllis Balch; and *A Clinician's Guide to Holistic Medicine* by Robert A.

Anderson, M.D. See the Readings and References appendix for more information.

Also, remember that our "nourishment" comes from sources other than those we eat and drink. We ingest via our thoughts, emotions, and senses. So take care to nourish yourself mindfully in all these domains. It is possible to be overfed and undernourished.

## II. Physical Activity

The body is our home for our adventure on Earth. We must treat it with honor and respect or we will find ourselves without a place to live. As our vehicle for life's journey, the body must be well maintained in order to allow us to live our dream and manifest our gifts and talents.

Physical activity is one of the most important parts of any self-care program. Your body wants to be used, not saved. Exercise is a powerful force in the management of weight loss, cardiovascular health, depression, and stress. In fact, long-term weight management demands exercise as part of any successful regimen.

The benefits of exercise are most dramatic when comparing the well-being of the couch potato and the walker—not the walker and the marathon runner. In other words, you don't have to spend endless hours at the gym to achieve results. Walking, climbing stairs, and household activities like vacuuming and dancing count, too. Don't forget to stretch and rest, or the exercise might create as many problems as it helps. The practices of yoga, T'ai Chi, and Chi Kung are especially beneficial. You may need supervision via doctor or trainer, depending on the state of your health.

A daily moderate dose is safer and more beneficial than a large weekend dose. Weekend Warriors, beware! Variety is the spice of life when it comes to exercise. A varied program including cardiovascular work, weight training, agility, and stretching is more likely to become a real part of your daily life. Not only is it okay for your exercise program to be fun, it is mandatory for a sustainable plan. The best exercise is the one you do!

Don't forget that your brain and mind require exercise too. Using the mind—from puzzles to philosophizing—may lessen the risk of dementia.

To balance our physical activity and exercise, we need to insure adequate rest and sleep. Seven to nine hours of sleep are usually recommended. Inadequate sleep leads to chronic sleep deprivation which is a recognized health hazard. If the amount and patterns of your sleep are compromised, you are putting your well-being at risk and should seek expert help. In the meantime, never underestimate the value of a good night's sleep or a nap.

Useful references include: *Body, Mind and Sport: the Mind-Body Guide to Lifelong Fitness* and *Your Personal Best* by John Douillard; *Wellness Medicine* by Robert A. Anderson, M.D.; *Women's Bodies, Women's Wisdom* by Christine Northup, M.D.; and *The Wellness Guide to Lifelong Fitness* by T.P. White.

## III. Contemplation and Solitude:
## The Inner Life

The deep inner dimension of our existence and the vast expanse and unseen presence that surrounds our physical bodies cannot be discounted in any quest for health and healing.

In accessing our inner dimension, one overriding principle is "silence is golden." Time for quiet and solitude is absolutely unavoidable in your self-care program and is at the heart of stress management. As our dietary sources provide nutrients and energy for our external, physical world, slowing down and finding quiet are where the resources for the nourishment for our inner life come. In times of personal and global tension, fear, despair, and longing, our inner life needs to be attended to as carefully as our outer life. Reading classic works and the "masters" can provide respite and wisdom. Daily exposure to words of wisdom is a needed antidote to the barrage of television "info-tainment" and the heavy overstimulation that modern communication provides our senses.

Many excellent references are available, including:

- *Sabbath: Restoring the Sacred Rhythm of Rest*, Wayne Muller
- *The Miracle of Mindfulness*, Thich Nhat Hanh
- *Wherever You Go—There You Are*, Jon Kabat-Zinn
- *A Path with Heart*, Jack Kornfield
- *Don't Just Do Something—Sit There*, Sylvia Boorstein

- *Walking a Sacred Path*, Lauren Artress
- *Anam Cara: A Book of Celtic Wisdom*, John O'Donohue
- *The Power of Now*, Eckhart Tolle

Each of us needs to escape the incessant noise that surrounds us—everyday business, social chatter, mass media—to create the opening to connect with our inner wisdom. This is where our deep learning takes place. It is our well of inner wisdom that informs us of our life's dream, and guides us toward it slowly and steadily. As we begin to silence the usual din around us and lessen the distractions that keep us from our vital inner work, we will better hear the inner messages that can show us our choices and determine the path to our real lives.

Insight meditation teacher Jack Kornfield teaches about inner knowing. He tells a story about finding yourself in a very difficult situation—one that calls for more wisdom than you are able to tap at the time. Imagine you hear a knock on the door and you open it. There stands _____ (fill in the blank with the guide you need: Jesus, Buddha, Mother Teresa, Gandhi, etc.). Let them trade places with you for a moment, taking your role in the situation. They will advise you about what to do next.

As you fill yourself with the way you imagine they would handle the knotty situation, you realize how much more potential for wisdom we carry than what we usually realize. My older son, when confronted with a problem beyond his skill in Little League baseball, often conjured advice from the baseball sages of days gone by, wondering, "What would Babe Ruth do at a time like this?"

## Finding Time

Exactly what you do with the solitude you create is less important than making the time for it. This time is never wasted. It is as important as mealtime. It is best not diluted by doing anything else, including vigorous exercise (though exercise can be mind-freeing and mind-emptying and provide another wonderful opportunity for clear internal dialogues and expression).

Whether you sit, stand, lie, or walk; recite an affirmation or mantra, chant, pray, or count your breathing; open or close your eyes, do yoga, meditation, or music, the essential thing is to quiet the mind and be fully in the moment. Stay with the peace and calm of the present. Don't fight the thoughts that show up; let them pass. Don't resist the sounds you hear; let them be. Don't fight the restlessness you feel; just be with it.

Start to keep a daily appointment with yourself to be alone, quiet, present, aware, and mindful. To start, make an appointment as short as necessary to insure you will do it. Then gradually increase your time commitment as the rewards from this quiet time are experienced. Practice, persevere, and continue trying.

Disconnect the quiet practice from any particular goal. Do it for its own intrinsic worth—your full awareness. Whether you have five minutes or sixty minutes, start with whatever time you have. We can experience the effects of these practices—even in *one minute*. These "magic moments" of silence, breath awareness, focused attention, relaxation, body scanning, etc., can give us a taste of what the benefits of a longer, engaged practice might provide.

## The Deep Minute

The use of frequent deep minutes—directed at the experience of calmness, relaxation, awareness, appreciation, gratitude, clarity, forgiveness, intention, anger management, stress reduction, conflict resolution, deep listening, inspiration, creativity, and imagination—acts as an entry point to *changing our minds* one minute at a time. Thus, we begin to practice new behaviors that truly are health creating, sustainable, and transformative.

Entering a deep minute simply involves taking the time in the course of a busy day to pause, bringing attention—for just a minute—to the desired subject and quietly allowing an opening for a mindful break in whatever is going on. It can be done at your desk, on the job, alone, or in a group, with eyes open or closed. All that is necessary is your full attention. What is gained is equanimity. What it leads to are longer periods of non-reactive balance in your daily life. Here is a practice that is a small, early step toward enduring wisdom practice. A deep minute can be used whenever, wherever, and for whatever you decide. All you need to do is do it!

Every minute is a new creative experience, never lived before, never to be lived again. Every moment that we enter with full awareness is a true gift and a practice of being present and mindful.

Mindful of what actually *is* (the present)—not what *was* (the past) or what *might be* (the future)—living in the moment, minute by minute, is a *wisdom practice*. Since it is your practice, it will not be judged and cannot be compared to anyone else's. But you must be present to win! This cannot be replaced by exercise or sleep. The practice is about

being awake—fully awake, fully present in the
moment, and quiet.

As you practice, you will notice your mind's
thought process settling like mud in agitated water.
You will begin to gain awareness of your bodily
sensations and emotions—your visceral responses to
what happens around you. You will be in better
touch with yourself and your environment. Can you
be patient and wait for the mud to settle and the
water to clear?

The practices taught in meditation classes,
stress reduction centers, behavior modification
programs, yoga classes, and the like provide
technical instructions in quieting the mind. These
instructive moments need to spread into our "real
lives" and not just be something we do once a week
during group or class time.

Mindfulness is being fully present with whatever
you are doing—sitting, jogging, eating, washing the
dishes, cleaning up a mess, talking with a friend,
negotiating a deal, listening to a sales pitch, driving
a car, or even working at your job. These activities
can all be done mindfully—that is, with your full
attention. Even when you are remembering the
lessons of the past or planning the future, do it from
the context of the present. We plan or remember,
not only as a distraction from our present reality,
but as an active experience of our now.

A stress reduction group, yoga class or daily
quiet time may become additions to the to-do list.
On top of family and professional obligations, they
may actually lead us to more agitation, rather than
less. You will need to make choices and set priorities
within your limits. How do you go about making
choices? What guides your decisions?

## Setting Priorities and Making Decisions

We each have a full gamut of aspirations. Some are lofty, some practical. We have a plethora of possible actions; some are loud and demanding, others more remote and perhaps more alluring. What to do? If we can make choices that are consistent with our underlying philosophy or perspective, they will be decisions that are health creating and life sustaining. We need a philosophy that braids our scientific and spiritual legacies, that acknowledges our biology and our life story. This will bring us to insightful thinking, compassionate feeling, and service-oriented action. This perspective will support a balanced daily existence—not free of difficult choices or conflict, but consistent with our personal vision.

These questions can help guide your decision-making process:

- Does the decision feel right?
- Does it seem rational?
- Is it consistent with your concept of truth?
- Is it in line with your integrity?
- Is it sustainable for your personal economy, for the environment, and for future generations?

Special note: If you hear a voice of doubt, even far in the distance, don't ignore it. Listen to it early in your decision process—it may be your own internal voice of wisdom you are hearing.

## IV. Relationship and Community:
## When Two or More Are Gathered

True independence is a myth. There is a power and intelligence of great profundity in the creation of community. The recognition of our ultimate interconnections and interdependence and the development of effective communication skills and practices are deep medicine.

Relationship is an essential part of the healing journey and of all healing encounters. The most important relationship of all is with yourself. From that relationship, we build the others. A certain amount of time spent with others is necessary for health. Social isolation is a risk factor for heart disease as significant as smoking, and a supportive community is a powerful healing force.

Make time to be with others on a one-to-one basis and in groups. Walk your dog. Stroke your cat; inter-species relationships are important, too. And so are inter-generational contacts. Visit with an elder; they have much to teach us that our youth-oriented culture disregards. Enjoy the company of a child; they need the guidance, we need the fun. Practice direct communications in your intimate and group relationships. Make amends. Forgive an indiscretion.

Avoid gossip and harboring resentments until they boil into something scalding and become very hard to clean up.

Move your relational work beyond your inner circle of family and friends. True compassion and caring for others cannot be boundaried by our intimates, but must extend to all our relations and the greater good.

Communication skills are essential to healthy relationships. There is probably no knowledge base more resonant or skill set more valuable than those related to direct, honest, timely communications. Check in frequently for clarification when you have doubts about what was said, heard, or happened. Don't make assumptions or speculate; ask for confirmation or repeat back what you think you heard.

Very valuable learning tools for communications include an audio tape set by Patrick O'Neil of Toronto, Canada, entitled *Extraordinary Conversations.* The books, CDs, and tapes of Angeles Arrien, and the book *Difficult Conversations: How to Discuss What Matters Most,* by Stone, Patton, and Heen, are also highly recommended.

## Wilderness Experience

When it comes to regulating the rhythm of our lives in a health-creating way, a relationship to nature's cycles can be a more meaningful timekeeper than our wristwatches, electronic calendars, and alarm clocks. Nature's usual pace is medium to slow. High-speed activities, such as chasing prey, last only for brief periods of time. In contrast, our usual pace is fast to overwhelmed. One of the most rejuvenating aspects of my vacations is the chance to allow my body to function at its own rhythm without external aids. A health-creating holiday is one where I get up when I am through sleeping, eat when I feel hungry, and follow a schedule based on internal requirements rather than external demands.

Time in natural settings reconnects us to our roots and rhythms in Mother Nature. It is time when we can reacquaint ourselves with aspects of our being that may go unvisited during our usual day-to-day life in the working world. We can go alone or with a group, formally or informally. The wilderness experience is conducive to giving gratitude, seeking guidance, acknowledging, connecting, and regaining perspective. It provides us opportunity for ritual and ceremony, two essential ingredients for reverent, mindful, healthy living. Walking in the woods, ascending a mountain, swimming in the ocean, napping on a beach, working in the garden, watching a sunrise or sunset, listening to a babbling brook, feeling the dew on your bare feet or the wind in your face are all experiences that refresh the spirit and create openings for growth and healing. Make time to be in nature on a daily basis—even if you only walk around the block.

## Work-Play Alignment

Ancient humans didn't spend all their time hunting and cooking and seeking shelter. There was also a certain amount of time sitting around the fire, dancing, and storytelling. According to many, they spent a good bit more time in leisure activities than we do—even with our so-called labor-saving and time-saving devices.

Work dominates our contemporary lives. We work not only to provide our material needs, but to define self-image and give us a sense of worth. However, we are neither our accomplishments nor our mistakes. And we are not "wasting time" when we are at play or at rest. Adjusting your concept of productive time to include play is essential. Playtime needs to be nourishing, not mind-deadening (such as watching more television) or thrill-seeking (the "adventure-junkie syndrome"). To balance our relationship to work with sufficient rest and reflection, we need to spend some of our time nurturing our inner needs and recharging the batteries, not competing in performance-oriented, approval-generating settings.

## Daily Blessings

We have many opportunities during the course of our daily lives to honor our journey on earth. The simplest acts—retiring in the evening, arising in the morning, preparing or eating a meal—all give us the opportunity to pause, set intention, and give thanks. In so doing, we make activities that otherwise might seem humdrum or mundane into activities that are sacred, purposeful, and meaningful.

Doing something purposefully can turn it into a personal ritual. Personal rituals support our well-being by slowing us down, allowing us to honor, give gratitude, pray, or reflect. This is the most pragmatic definition of mindfulness. Being mindful is doing whatever it is one is doing with attention to the task and intention to create a real purpose for the task. Furthermore, mindful practice of our daily activities makes us responsible for our actions.

By slowing down and doing something in a meaningful way, we begin to create sacred time and space, we begin to experience the connection and interplay with all around us. For example, contemplating a small seed can connect us with the potential inherent in beginnings and the future. Mindfully approaching a meal can connect us with the incredible network that brought it to us.

Starting with the earth, sun, and water necessary for the food's growth, we can imagine the farmer, the picker of the fruit, and the baker of the bread. Then there are their families, and the transporters, processors, sellers, and on and on. How incredibly interconnected our lives are. Even if we raised the produce for our salad in our own garden, the connections and relationships are just as extensive.

### Mindful Washing: Shower Yourself with Love

A perfect opportunity for personal health-creating ritual occurs every morning after we arise from a night's sleep and begin our preparation for the new day. Our daily morning ablutions are an occasion for physical/mental/emotional/spiritual practice and communion with all around us.

First resting quietly for a few moments in bed after awakening is a chance to give gratitude for our reawakening—not just to review the day's to-do list. Then, our morning shower is an opportunity to become better acquainted with our physical bodies. We can take a shower for better reasons than to smell good for someone else or to rinse off the daily grime or night's sleep.

A shower is also a time to thank our bodies for the daily miracles they provide. If we perform a mindful shower we will be touching and acknowledging all parts of our bodies. If we do it purposefully rather than mindlessly, we create a sacred few moments that can set our tone for the remainder of the day (or evening if we are showering after a day's work). The shower routine then becomes a personal ritual. Our shower can also provide us an opportunity for a full-body stretch, a stimulating rubdown, and a few moments to welcome ourselves to the new day and reacquaint ourselves with ourselves. Shower yourself with love.

When beginning the shower, it helps to begin washing at the extremities and work toward the core of the body. This is not unlike the pathway selected when one walks a labyrinth: walking first from the outside or external into the central or internal. In the center, we pause for a moment. This reminds us of the need for rest, quiet, and renewal. With the insight from the interior, we slowly walk again to the outer ring of the labyrinth. This approach is a powerful metaphor for the healing path and also works in the shower. Each body part should be attentively approached and touched. Gratitude can be given for the role it plays. The skin can be caressed or vigorously rubbed. Sore spots can be identified, tender areas recognized and acknowledged.

If you begin soaping yourself from the feet, you can bend over and touch your toes. (If that stretch is too long, lift your foot onto a ledge or bend your knee to allow yourself to reach your toes.) The toes can be spread apart and each individual toe stretched. The sole can be vigorously rubbed, as can the top of the foot to awaken to the day of locomotion and to honor it for the many times it strikes the ground to move us from one task or interaction to another. We can then work our way up through the ankle, lower leg, and calf to the knee joint and the thighs and the hips, and thank our legs for their support and for hauling us about.

As we work upward from the feet toward the heart, we must not forget the back of the body. It's often easier to reach the front surfaces and more difficult to reach the back surfaces where we cannot see. It is important that we also access those areas that are not seen and are hard to reach so that they too are acknowledged, their contributions recognized, and their secrets and needs accessed.

After the legs, attend to the upper extremities (arms). Some may prefer to start with the hands and arms. When working with the hands it can be good to lift them up to chest level, to eye level, or even above the head. Where the hands are held, where the arms are positioned, affects the physicality of the action. Raising the arms increases the cardiovascular work involved. Each finger can be rubbed, spread apart, bent forward, and bent backward. The hands can be interlaced and lifted high above the head with the palms down and then lifted high above the head with the palms up. Then they can be placed downward in front and behind the body with the fingers interlaced palms up and palms down to provide another stretch.

As the arms are washed, the movement goes from hands toward shoulders and armpits. The shoulders and buttocks are two important areas where we need to reach behind ourselves to unseen areas. First lift the hand up overhead, bend the elbow and wash the shoulder and the back of the neck from behind. Then bring the hand and arm behind from below to wash the lower back and buttock. A movement similar to putting a wallet in a back pocket provides an excellent range of motion for the shoulder, elbow, and wrist. When washing the back it is useful to use a washcloth to allow one arm above to connect with the other arm below along the back, using the washcloth as a connecting strap. Each of the arms should be used first as the upper and then as the lower part of this backwashing maneuver. Moving the cloth from top to bottom as well as from side to side provides an excellent stretch across the shoulders and back.

When the head is washed and scrubbed, we can honor our eyes, nose, ears, mouth, teeth, and tongue. Our neck is recognized for holding up our head. Our head is honored for protecting our brain and its capacity to think clearly and feel fully. The communication system of neuronal connections within the brain and down the spinal cord and to all parts peripheral is an internal network of unfathomable complexity.

The greeting of the body should include the genital areas, chest, and belly. Acknowledge the breasts that give nourishment and the protective rib cage and breastbone. The lungs housed within the chest, which link our matter to life through the breath, can be remembered with several conscious breaths including the in-phase, out-phase, and intermediary pauses. The beating heart is both a pump for life-sustaining blood to all parts of the body and a mythic "seat" of our feelings and compassion. The vessels coursing away from and back to its four chambers create a tree-like network of "pickup and delivery" of amazing intricacy.

Rubbing the belly, we connect with our inner organs. The stomach and intestines will translate our food from external sources into fuel for our bodily processes. Sacred honor can be given to our liver, spleen, kidneys, adrenals, and pancreas that secrete necessary substances or eliminate toxic wastes harmful to our inner landscape. The sides of the body from armpit to hip on each side should be washed, recalling that the fringe worn by Native American peoples on the sides of their clothing was to ward off unseen attack from the side—or being sideswiped.

Once the initial soaping is completed, a thorough rinse allows us to repeat the routine from top to core and from bottom to core. If the washing phase was recognition of the physicality of the body, perhaps the rinsing phase can pay homage to the sacred nature of our body and its parts. For those who are conserving water, the soaping part can be done with the water turned off and then the water can be turned on again for the rinse phase. This, too, is a chance for mindful awareness of the limited resources that our planet provides us and our personal responsibility in their maintenance.

Once the rinse phase has been completed, we can again stimulate and acknowledge our bodies when we towel off and dry ourselves. We can begin at our toes or the fingertips and move gently or vigorously over our bodies to the central heart of our core. While doing so we can stretch, bless, pray, and remember to breathe with our attention directed mindfully.

Many of us lament the lack of time we have for even the most rudimentary exercise program. This simple approach allows us the possibility of completing a full range of motion and gentle stretching as part of our daily morning activity. If we are diligent about touching our toes, about stretching our arms, about twisting and rotating as we dry our backs, about raising our arms above our head, dropping them behind our back, lifting them up our back from below, we have begun to deliver on our agreement with ourselves to exercise.

Carrying this concept further—for example, to our formal exercise program (generally recommended to be done before the shower), to the

preparation of our morning meal, to our commute
to work, to our activities at work, and to our
relationships with our family and coworkers—can
have great benefits. As we mindfully approach our
routine activities, we turn them into sacred
functions and health-creating actions. This is how
meaningful change occurs: small steps done
repeatedly with care and understanding.
Recognizing the benefits that they bring, we will not
only feel better, we will feel better about ourselves.

After the toweling off and drying, and before
getting dressed, we could enhance the ritual by
"anointing" ourselves with powder or oil or water in
areas where we seek healing or guidance or
understanding. For example, our eyes could be
anointed and blessed as we seek to see that which is
good in other people as we go forward in our day.
We could anoint our armpits and sides and pray to
be spared "sneak attacks" from any direction. We
could anoint our ears so that we may listen to others
well and without judgment. We could touch areas of
our body that are injured or uncomfortable or in
need of healing, and ask that they be rested and
given what they need to repair themselves and
restore function to our normal levels.

## Nothing External Can Fill an Internal Need

When we bring this kind of clear attention to our
daily activities, from exercise to eating to working to
playing, we will experience the health benefits that
come with mindful living. We will exercise more
often because it makes us feel better. Our eating will
modulate as we deal with more than the accounting
of calories and pounds, but engage the whens and

whys of our eating from physical hunger to emotional hunger. As we become intimate with our own bodies and their functions, our capacity to be intimate with others will also benefit.

As we gain experience with our personal rituals, we may choose to include a moment of personal silence as part of our morning routine. Taking a moment or two in the beginning of the day to breathe quietly and naturally may be another "routine" that can add a sense of sacredness to the day.

Our breath connects us to life. Breathing with intention, slowly, naturally, aware of the inhalation and the pause and the exhalation, can calm the nervous system and allow a quieting of the generalized chatter that surrounds us. When that chatter quiets, for even a brief moment, we have a chance to listen to our inner voice.

Some have found it valuable to create a small altar somewhere in their homes—a place where ancestors, friends, and family members can be remembered and honored, a site where milestones can be recalled with a small memento. Visiting your altar as part of a morning routine can provide a time and place to pray for others who are ill or in need of guidance, and to speak the names of loved ones to be remembered—loved ones who may be struggling with problems or illness.

At the altering moment of silence that we experience at our personal altar, we can also consider what lies ahead of us in the coming day and what resource or strength will serve us best. Perhaps we need flexibility, perhaps we need our sense of humor; maybe our patience will be tested in the schedule that awaits us. Whatever it might be, we can ask for help and prepare ourselves for what is to come. As we do this, it is important to recognize that the agenda and the game plan that we have in mind may not be exactly what happens, or what the universe/mystery/Divine has on tap for us. We need always be open to what may show up, not just what we expect to take place. Oftentimes, our expectations set us up for failure or unhappiness or disappointment. Rather, we must be keenly aware of the potential for things not going as we expect. We need to maintain an attitude of curiosity and our sense of humor as we move forward.

## Finding the Way

Another way people seek guidance is the use of various oracle-based wisdom, such as Tarot cards, animal medicine cards, angel cards, the I-Ching hexagrams, and other age-old formats where questions can be asked. Perhaps the most common form of this activity is the horoscope often found in magazines and in the daily newspaper. Although these practices are often labeled New Age, these practices are anything but new. Many have histories of thousands of years of application in the lives of many people from many cultures.

When we use these techniques, we need to trust the wisdom that leads us to choose the card or reading that we select—or that selects us. Then we must be curious and flexible in the way that we interpret how it may apply to our individual circumstances. Certainly, some of the messages we find could be applied, in a generic way, to most anyone, so many people dismiss the information that comes their way from these sources.

Nonetheless, there is always some applicable wisdom to be found, even if it feels totally contrary to our present situation.

As we seek guiding information, we might also try recalling our dreams. In the dreamtime, when much of our activity is suspended during sleep, we may be visited by allies in human, animal, or situational form. The knowledge they impart during our sleeping lives can help illuminate our waking lives. Being attentive to these messages, perhaps even recording them, can be a powerful source of insight.

Virtually any practice that helps us to be in touch with our true selves can be a health-creating or healing endeavor. Expanded or more focused applications of these sample mindful practices—such as a regular exercise program, the formal practice of yoga or T'ai Chi, or a defined time for philosophic readings, contemplation, or prayer—are all opportunities of celebration, blessing, and reverence for the activities that make up our lives. These brief moments of experience may lead to a desire for more activities that afford us the time and space for personal exploration and growth. And this will lead us to teachers and mentors, who are also essential as we explore our paths to health and healing.

Teachers take many forms. Anyone from a fitness trainer to a nutritional counselor to a yoga teacher to an important stranger can stimulate self-exploration and change. Periods of retreat and intensive learning can also be valuable punctuators of our schedules. They provide time, content, and context for new learning—and time will also be needed afterward to integrate the learnings into our daily lives.

Whenever there are learnings and apparent progress, there will also be setbacks, stumbling, new questions, and the need for new learning and processing of our latest experiences. You'll learn and relearn that it is the process that is important, and it is the "road" rather than the "destination" that we relish. We also need to remind ourselves that it is the recurrent, daily chores and events that give form to our lives. We don't have to be doing heroic, dramatic, momentous tasks to be living healing, loving lives. Our acts of unseen, simple loving kindness as friends, parents, colleagues, and caregivers are likely to be the flour from which our life's bread is baked and the greatest source of our physical and spiritual healing for others and ourselves.

## The Lessons of a Day Trip

All day-trippers—walkers, hikers, drivers, cyclists, paddlers, sailors—appreciate the steps and nuances of planning and executing a journey. We can learn from these defined excursions as we plot and pursue our personal path to health and healing.

First, it's necessary to have a goal in mind, whether it is the top of a mountain, a certain distance, or particular time frame. We can plan most appropriately when we have an endpoint in our sights. Will we be out for one hour or eight? What is the weather forecast? Will foul weather gear be needed? How much food and water? While we are planning, we must be fully aware of the possibilities, probabilities, and goals. Once our course is plotted, provisions secured, equipment checked out, and skill set in place, we can set out.

It is at this point that I find it extremely helpful to break the journey into very manageable pieces or steps. Getting to the starting point and launching are two obvious milestones in any journey. As I proceed, particularly if the going is tough, I seldom look to the final destination or goal, but rather mark my progress with very short milestones.

If, for example, I am pedaling up a very long, steep hill, my goal may be no farther ahead than several yards! At such times, I appreciate the road (the process), not the inn (the endpoint), and understand what it means to be fully invested in what I am doing, sure that I am rightly placed and not attached to the outcome. If I become very tired, the weather turns ominous, or my bicycle chain breaks, I must be prepared to relinquish my preconceived destination for the time being and take proper care of the situation at hand.

In circumstances where our preconceived goal seems thwarted, we are likely to feel frustrated, angry, or upset. It is precisely in these situations that we can best practice balance and equanimity. By bringing curiosity and inquiry to the setting instead of anger and frustration, we can be constructive rather than destructive.

In *Wisdom of Insecurity*, Alan Watts states that we are only ever in "control" to a point. In the final analysis, it is our attitude over which we have the most control. Unexpected external influences constantly show up on our paths, as do internal moods, energy swings, doubts, fears, motivations, drives, and exuberance. The crispness of the air, the grandeur of the view, the exhilaration of the climb may move and inspire us. The cold wind, dark cloud, seemingly insurmountable obstacle may put us off.

Each requires our awareness, attention, action, and sense of awe. Each requires us to be flexible enough to alter our course with changing circumstances. Flexibility and the capacity to change are essential.

These day trips are opportunities for practice and inner and outer strength-building on our path of discovery toward our optimal state of health and healing.

*Life has meaning only in the struggles.*
*Triumph or defeat is in the hands of the gods.*
*So let us celebrate the struggles.*

**– Swahili Warrior Song**
From *Prayers for Healing*, Maggie Oman (ed.)

## A Workout for "Inner" Strength

We spend a great deal of time and money working out—exercising, bodybuilding, stretching. Most of these activities are directed primarily at our outer strength. What about building our inner strength? How do we forge the endurance for inner challenges? How do we develop the flexibility, agility, and strength to deal with habits, behaviors, fears, and stresses that trouble us with or without accompanying physical or mental health issues?

We need workouts, exercises and practices for growing our inner resources as well as our outer, external strengths. We must always stay alert to how these practices can be weapons, addictions, and obstacles—not just tools and aids—if they are misused.

Interestingly, we often seek in the wrong places. We look for activities that allow us to distract ourselves from the necessary work, or numb ourselves to the inner pain, or insulate ourselves from the emptiness or injury we may feel. Material goods, lofty ideals, or so-called spiritual practices sought without doing our inner personal strength-building will not fill us, heal us, or protect us.

Building inner strength requires us to:

- become aware of patterns, behaviors, habits, attitudes, thoughts, feelings, and actions that are burdening, obstructing, poisoning, or deterring us;
- bring our attention to issues to be addressed;
- determine appropriate action steps to engage and begin remedying the issue;
- maintain curiosity, wonder, and awe at our progress (or lack thereof) and the unfolding of our lives.

The inner workout requires practicing *awareness* (being present, awake), focusing our *attention*, taking *action,* and a childlike sense of *awe.* These practices are not just to make us feel good, but they generally are good for us.

Many tools and practices can move us toward the goal of building inner strength by helping us develop self-knowledge, trust, and respect. These practices require discipline to begin and sustain. That is, an overt act of will is required. A faith that the path has the potential to lead to a desired outcome—even as we pursue the path detached from a specific outcome—is also a necessary ingredient in inner strength building. We commit to the path or process, not just the goal or outcome.

We know course correction is part of the process. This brings renewed meaning to the statement that we each are a work in progress. So as you move along your personal path of discovery toward health, choose teachers, practices, and tools, and use them wisely and respectfully so they heal, not hinder or hide. As these choices are made and practices undertaken, be gentle with yourself.

Celebrate your successes, no matter how modest. Note how far you have come rather than how far you have left to go.

## Lifelong Learning

On our paths, we need teachers, guides, role models, and mentors. Different guides are needed at different times. As the Zen saying reminds us, "When the student is ready, the teacher appears."

During some stages of life, we process knowledge or integrate lessons, and may have no need or desire for formal instruction. At other times, group or individual learning crucibles will be essential. Ultimately, we craft our own mosaic from the materials we have gathered and the teachers who have influenced us.

I have had many teachers to whom I am eternally grateful. My parents, my wife of more than thirty-five years, and my children and grandchildren have contributed mightily to my education and ongoing evolution. By modeling, challenging, supervising, inspiring, loving, pushing buttons, and pulling chains, they are guides of mythical proportion. My school teachers, college professors, medical school and postgraduate training instructors prodded, cajoled, and filled me with facts, figures, and a strong work ethic. Religious men and women, philosophers and thinkers, physicists and friars, friends, colleagues, neighbors and important strangers have all fostered my learning. Adversaries, competitors, naysayers, skeptics and antagonists have also been teachers of great import, in their own ways.

Think about those who have been important teachers on your learning curve of life. Think about those for whom you have been an influential teacher. Remember a few of your most pivotal lessons, where they occurred, how you felt and how they impacted your life.

## A Personal Story:
## Never Tire of New Sources of Wisdom

Not long ago I had the privilege of attending a retreat as part of the transformative work done by the Institute of Noetic Sciences in Petaluma, California. One of the exercises involved taking time in silence on the beautiful rolling hills that surround its campus. We were sent out onto the land with a ceremony that included drumming and the use of one of the oldest tools of indigenous cultures, the rattle. We were given several questions to contemplate and advised to be alert and attentive to the signs that the land might present to us to help us with the questions we were contemplating.

I set off with lofty expectations. What powerful allies might make themselves visible to me? What wisdom would the call of Brother Raven or the Spirit of Native Peoples previously on this land reveal? As I began my meditative walk, I was drawn to a fallen, partially uprooted tree. While some branches were dead or dying, others were clearly green and robust. I was moved to notice that forces act on us which can significantly disrupt our roots and direction. Some parts of us die along the way. We have different uses at different times. But I felt that this was not the place for me to stop.

I carried on farther until I came to a fenced boundary of the property. The fence called me to respect the limits and boundaries of the collective, myself, and others. As I climbed higher on the hillside, I could hear the noise from the freeway not far from the entrance to the natural wooded enclave. Slightly higher on the hill, I could look down and into the distance and see the dense line of cars on the highway—a technological river flowing slowly toward San Francisco. I imagined the stress the slow traffic was causing. I could almost hear the din of engaged cell phones and feel the sense of urgency those trapped in the gnarled, phlegmatic, bumper-to-bumper crawl were experiencing. "Leave the collective trance. Don't be confined by what seems to be so important—look further," was the message for me.

I continued my silent wandering. As I walked, I waited for a vision more profound than the freeway, a symbol more remarkable than a fence, a helping ally more dignified than a lizard sunning on a dull, flat rock. Where were soaring raven, illusive mountain lion?

On up the hill toward the summit I moved—expectations ablaze. When the top was crested and I could see a 360-degree panorama, I was shocked to see a large, abandoned tractor tire! How disappointing. Others had been here before, and this was not an artifact to be cherished—or was it? Amused, I sat down on the large, black remnant of previous visitors to my chosen destination. As I surveyed the hilltop, I noticed that there was a message for me encoded on my perch. "Goodyear," it read. A *good year*—how prophetic. My curiosity aroused, I wondered what else the circular oracle might reveal. I swept its dusty surface. My dig was rewarded as more advice appeared. While a good year was prominently predicted, some cautions were also noted when I read that, "Failure may be due to misapplication, improper inflation (over or under-inflation), overloading, excessive speed, and improper mounting."

What germane and powerful wisdom! How different its source than my romantic expectations. How interesting when and where we can find wisdom if we are open to seeing it and hearing it. The distant drumbeat beckoned me to return to the circle of my colleagues to share our journeys. I descended the hill once again, surprised and moved by the wisdom in nothing special and every moment.

*...being no one special ...*
*just the space in which creation is unfolding.*

**– Taoist** *(source unknown)*

## A Mystery, Not a Puzzle

At some point, in the course of our health, illness, and healing, we confront the reality of the inevitability of death. Buddhist teacher and author Sogyal Rinpoche has written, "Learn to die and thou shalt learn how to live. There shall none learn how to live that hath not learned how to die."

Living a fully engaged life requires us to coexist with the uncertainty and anxiety of one of the keystone mysteries of our existence. Health doesn't mean avoiding death or even postponing it.

Health does involve coming to terms with death, though our society tends to deny it. Consider the cosmetology of funeral parlors; the facelifts, hair transplants, and tummy tucks of cosmetic surgery; and the wrinkle creams and dyes of beauty salons.

Hundreds of thousands of people die each day. Millions each year. We all show signs of death's impending, although unpredictable, arrival, as age sculpts our bodies. As a culture, we tend to see death as an end, a terminal event, a tragedy, a failure, or a loss. In other traditions, however, death is often viewed as merely leaving or dropping the physical body. It is as much a beginning as an ending. It is seen as another threshold in the mysterious journey of which the bodily existence is only a part.

The inevitability of death is coupled with the unpredictability of exactly when it will occur. True, someone with end-stage cancer may be more likely to die than a teenaged gymnast. However, lightning does strike and remarkable remissions are possible. Not knowing which day or hour will be the last raises the stakes. We are urged not to waste our precious time. We are called to cherish each moment, to value the ordinary and the extraordinary, to use our lives well. We need to seize the day, be here now, and gratefully honor the gift of our time inhabiting a body here on Earth.

A painting resides over my office desk by author and artist Brian Andreas, which informs my daily choices and priorities. His whimsical watercolor of a dancing figure is captioned, "His life changed the day he realized he only had time for the important things."

At a workshop I once attended, one of the participants prepared a hilarious song to send our group on its separate ways, called *This Life Is No Rental*. He was right. It is ours alone. We can't return it for another one. There are no instant replays or retakes or rehearsals. Nobody knows when the last act will be performed. As a favorite saying reminds me, "Life is uncertain, eat dessert first!" So don't save the frosting for the end.

We fear death in part because of our attachment to the concept of the physical body. Our perceived separation from the natural cycles of nature also distances us from the role of death. Yet all that surrounds us is transitory. Even mountains don't last forever.

Many descriptions exist from many sources on what happens after death. Our beliefs and faith define our view. For all we know, death may be a continuation of life in some undivulged form. It is a mystery. A mystery—not a puzzle. We will not find one single missing piece that explains all, that odd-shaped piece that has fallen off the table and been swept unknowingly under the rug. We exist in an unfinished riddle, the solution of which is not soon to be revealed. This mystery encompasses not only death but the time before birth.

We cannot know about those times, but we can coexist with their mystery. We will never have all the answers, but being comfortable with good questions is an important part of our human condition.

A cartoon I saw recently offered a good answer to an old question:

*Q: Do you believe in life after death?*
*A: I believe in life before death!*

*Move from within*
*Don't move the way fear wants you to*
*Begin a foolish project*
*Noah did.*

**– Rumi**

## Becoming Aware, Taking Action

I am deeply grateful for the insights and teaching of Angeles Arrien. She is a cultural anthropologist, healer, and educator whose work reveals the relevance of the wisdom of indigenous peoples to our contemporary lives. Her *Four-Fold Way* is a model of a wisdom path. Her books, retreats, and workshops are rich resources for self-awareness, spiritual wisdom, social consciousness, and healing.

In her approach, Angeles honors the health of the inner house of ourselves and the outer house of the world in which we live. Her goal is to reunite us with our ecological and cultural roots. She describes archetypes that take the form of warrior, healer, visionary, and teacher. These provide a context for a healing journey.

### Warrior

The way of the warrior is about the skill of leadership. It is the power that resides in showing up—in being fully present. It is about learning to communicate clearly in our relationships and bringing groups to consensus. It is the power that resides in taking a stand.

### Healer

The way of the healer involves caring for our own health and for the well-being of others. It teaches how to draw the proper boundaries and limits in our relationships and to recognize what is meaningful in our lives.

Angeles teaches eight universal healing principles, found in many cultures. When we do not fully attend to these principles, we find ourselves on the shadow side of the healer archetype. Study the list below, and assess for yourself where you are supporting your health and well-being and where you are not attending to healthcare issues.

Supportive of health and well-being:

1. Balanced diet
2. Daily and weekly exercise
3. Time for fun, play, and laughter
4. Music, songs, or chanting
5. Love, touch, and support systems
6. Engaging in interests, hobbies, and creative purpose
7. Nature, beauty, and healing environments
8. Faith and belief in the supernatural

## Visionary

The path of the visionary teaches us to tell the truth and to speak and act with authenticity. The visionary archetype teaches us to act in ways that bring our dreams into the world.

## Teacher

The teacher demonstrates the art of passing on wisdom without attachment to any one way of doing things. It is about being open to, not attached to, outcome. We express the way of the teacher through constructive communication.

## The Four-Fold Way

Each of us has within us aspects of each of the four archetypes in varying proportions. Some may be overdeveloped, others underdeveloped. Balance is a goal. The principles/practices of *The Four-Fold Way* in application to our daily lives challenge us to:

- Show up—choose to be fully present (Warrior).
- Pay attention—listen to what has heart and meaning (Healer)
- Tell your truth without blame or judgment (Visionary)
- Be open to outcome, not attached to it (Teacher)

Further, we are challenged to:
- Say what is so, when it is so (tell the truth)
- Say what we mean (be in our integrity)
- Do what we say (build trust)

These practices build trust and safety through consistency and honesty. They are practices of *character development* and *mindfulness*. It is true that these principles require practice and skillful means. Learning and using them is richly rewarding.

## Seasonal Variation

One way that the cycles of nature influence our lives and well-being is through the changing seasons.

Fall is the time of harvest as well as letting go and new beginnings. We harvest crops, restart school, and celebrate the new year in many cultures. Winter is the time for reflection and contemplation. While the Earth's surfaces are covered with snow, animals hibernate and we are driven inside. Winter prepares us for the renewal and rebirth of Spring. Spring is the time of planting, nest-building, and relationship—when a young person's fancy turns. Spring is the time for remembering the healing power of love and renewing our commitment to health creation. Summer is a time of integration and coming into the full bloom of our life's dream and our authentic self. It is a time of reconnecting with nature's heat and our own fire and passion.

Angeles teaches us to bring character traits and action principles to bear in our lives in four domains. These are the domains of work and creativity; relationship; resources, prosperity and blessing; and health and vitality. They make up a fertile matrix, and offer powerful guidance in a rich interplay of healing.

Working with these principles can help translate aspirations and dreams into action. Many times the steps to fulfilling our dreams or responding to our calling will be small, mitigated by familial, financial, or other pressures. But little steps along the way are okay if they are in pursuit of a dream; they are actions that reduce anxiety and keep us in touch with innermost needs and desires.

It is our work to discover our unique inner gifts—our "medicine"—and to bring the medicine forward. No one can do it for us. No one can tell us what it should look like. We are offered the raw material and some rudimentary instructions, but we have to find the way ourselves.

This work is *deep medicine*. Medicine for our bodies, minds, and spirits. It is a lifelong process, during which we will be caught learning and need to course-correct many times. This deep work will be rewarded by the great wealth of energy it will attract to our pursuit of health and healing. What we give away in nonproductive behaviors and our quest for the elusive quick fix will be returned many fold in the sense of well-being that we will achieve along our path of self-discovery and self-expression.

---

⌘          **Exercise for Step Seven:**          ⌘
**Homeostasis**

---

Picture what steps are needed to realize your dream, desired breakthrough, or to reach your goal. Develop a timeline for each step to achieve your goal (what can you do in the next day, week, month, or year?). Then take the steps for the next day. Be prepared to repeat this exercise on a daily basis if necessary. Remember that our time is limited, and that we have windows of opportunity in which to act.

- Review the four pillars of self-care (nutrition, physical activity, contemplation/solitude, relationship/communication/community)— how are these pillars supporting your health foundation?
- Prioritize your health needs and what you need to do to take care of yourself. Consider the following:
  - Diet and eating habits. Is there a particular diet that interests you? Try it.
  - Relationship to work. Is your work health creating for you? Others?
  - Free time—how do you spend it? What activities nurture your well-being?
  - Interpersonal relationships—intimate (spouse, family), collective (work, group), spiritual (Divine, mystery). Do you have an adequate support system?

- In decision making, consider what best serves your:
  - Health
  - Truth
  - Intuition
  - Life's dream
- Five frogs are sitting on a log. Four decide to jump off. How many frogs are sitting on the log? (*Hint*: Is deciding the same as doing?)

- Consider various forms of healing or healthcare you've heard about; for example, contemporary Western medicine, traditional Chinese medicine, or Ayurvedic medicine. How do they fit with your belief system about health and healing? Do you need to get more information? If so, seek it—starting with the *Deep Medicine* Readings and References appendix, a library, a bookstore, or the Internet.

- Do any of the following questions and ideas seem to strike a chord within you? Pick a few and reflect on them for a moment—or make up a few of your own:
  - Do acupuncturists, chiropractors, massage therapists, yoga teachers, trainers, or martial arts instructors play a role in your health? Could they? If so, what appeals to you? Which would you like to sample first? Put it on your calendar.

- Make a list of all your good traits—your strengths and resources—and all your bad traits—your weaknesses and obstacles. Which list is longer? Does your self-assessment include as much praise as criticism?
- What are your current health fears? Create a plan to manage them.
- Do you express your authenticity? Have you experienced the consequences of not expressing what is true for you? Consider Abraham Maslow's insight: "If the essential core of the person is denied or suppressed, he gets sick, sometimes in obvious ways, sometimes in subtle ways, sometimes immediately, sometimes later...."
- Consider the meaning of the Native American declaration that "It's a good day to die."
- Consider what a seed gives up to become a sprout.
- Prepare and eat a meal mindfully, gracefully.
- Inventory your personal daily rituals that make your routine activities into sacred acts.
- Schedule a massage regularly—to help stay in touch with yourself.
- Practice saying no to others. It can be a complete sentence: "No."
- Practice saying yes to yourself (be as compassionate with yourself as with others).
- Practice really listening. When someone else is speaking, rather than rehearsing or thinking about what you are going to say next, listen attentively in such a way that you could reflect back to them what you've heard.
- Explain the saying: "Attitude is everything."

## Concepts for Self-Care and Choosing Health

These concepts are not rocket science and very likely your grandparents have given you the same advice.

- *Put your own oxygen mask on first.* Self-care comes first. This is generosity—not selfishness.

- *You are what you eat.* At a molecular, cellular level we literally become what we eat—so honor your intake.

- *Use it or lose it.* If you can do only one thing on your path to health—at whatever level—let exercise be the one thing. This goes for your body and your mind.

- *Silence is golden.* Quiet is essential to tapping into your inner wisdom and informing your actions.

- *It takes a village.* Relationship is at the core of our existence; relationship with self, intimate other, community, environment, and the Divine.

### Foundations for Self-Care

- Pay attention
- Slow down
- Be quiet
- Go inward

## Beginning a Daily Practice

Try starting your daily practice with Angeles Arrien's "Blessing Way"—

Each and every day...
- Give gratitude
- Set intention
- Perform a life-affirming action in support of your life's dream, passion, or calling.

# Epilogue: Equilibrium

---

A few years ago, I learned a valuable lesson in balance from a dear friend on a rocky beach surrounded by the natural beauty and grandeur of Flathead Lake in Montana. Sam had made his way to the shoreline early in the morning ahead of the rest of the group. There he had taken many of the grapefruit- and football-sized river rocks and balanced them on top of each other.

How could those smooth-surfaced, rounded, heavy lumps be made to stand upright on each other? Usually, only a small area of each rock was touching. Shapes were so irregular as to defy identifying them as geometric forms. Yet balance together at delicate points of contact, they did.

Sam beckoned me as I watched his play, inviting me to try. As a child, I likely would have run to try for myself. Yet as an adult, I was hesitant. I was skeptical that it was possible to get those irregular loads aligned and upright—concerned that I would fail. Cautiously, I eyed the balanced sculptures he was creating. Nervously, I lifted a rock, turned it over in my hands and looked for an appropriate site on which to place it. It fell to the left. I turned it, gently lifted and released, seeking its preferred orientation. I set it again and again, gently adjusting and aligning as it swayed and lurched in smaller arcs and smoother gestures. Then at one instant it paused in perfect balance—unwavering and erect like a ballerina *en pointe*. I sighed, stepping back to admire my work.

Seconds later, a movement stimulated my peripheral vision and I looked up to see Risky Business, our host's exuberant Labrador Retriever bounding eagerly toward me and my precariously balanced sculpture.

As his shiny wet body knocked down my carefully constructed monument, I surprised myself by laughing. The shift created in my consciousness by having done something that seemed impossible was too big to be washed away by the transient nature of the accomplishment. I set off to find more rocks, discover their centers, and stand them up. With quiet, gentle attention, I found their subtle balance points and mine.

Many times since, I have balanced rocks. The practice has been a quiet meditation, an inspiration, and a game. I have learned a great deal about balance—finding it, losing it, and finding it again. I have learned about impermanence and the transient nature of life, and about relationship—to myself, to the world around me, and to my work and companions.

In treating our illnesses and in creating our wellness, we are challenged to seek and maintain balance in our lives. As we struggle with our own unique path, we fashion formulas for well-being and living. In so doing, we develop our special talents so that we may then share with those around us. The coming together of many individual gifts in families and communities creates healing. My wish is that you will develop and bring your gifts to this evolving creation, contributing to your own health, the public health, and the healing of the planet.

# Afterword

Over the years of gestation of *Deep Medicine*, a visible change in thinking about health and disease has been occurring. Arenas as seemingly diverse as genetics, nutrition, and self-realization have found themselves fully in the public eye and medical consciousness as they come together in creative ways for medical treatments and new lifestyle approaches. For example, although fad diets continue to proliferate, it is clear no one diet can be right for everyone. Meanwhile, millions are drawn to the practices of yoga, meditation, T'ai Chi, and other wisdom practices seeking physical vitality, mental calm, and spiritual awareness.

As the public eats broccoli, savors the healthy fat of salmon, and attends stress management classes, new data are appearing in the medical literature supporting the power of lifestyle choices. Recommendations from such sources as the National Institutes of Health (NIH), the American Heart Association, the American Diabetes Association, and the American Cancer Society have described "therapeutic lifestyle change" as a "first line of therapy" and as a "standard of care" in the management of many conditions. Recently, light has been shed on a constellation of health risk factors known collectively as *metabolic syndrome*. This syndrome is characterized by abdominal obesity (increased waist circumference), elevated blood pressure, elevated blood lipids (fat), and elevated blood glucose (sugar). While it afflicts an estimated 50 million adults, metabolic syndrome is often without symptoms.

Metabolic syndrome is important because this combination of risk factors is related to the incidence of cardiovascular disease and stroke, diabetes, and cancer—the most common causes of annual mortality in the United States. The diseases associated with metabolic syndrome lead to a large percentage of U.S. healthcare costs. Increasingly healthcare plans and employers are looking for ways to reduce the healthcare cost burden. Part of this reduction can occur with intensive health risk factor modification. Because of this, lifestyle change programs are becoming a part of mainstream healthcare practice and are a key to healthier living in the future.

Improving our health depends not just on the availability of more general health information, but on the application of this information by individuals within the complexity of their own lives and in association with their own genetic individuality and personal preferences. Optimizing our genetic potential is a goal of practicing self-care and the thrust of a new scientific discipline called *nutrigenomics*. This term relates to understanding how gene expression is influenced by diet and nutrition. This line of study will likely have strong influence over what and how we eat and use supplements for the foreseeable future. Similar lines of inquiry may relate our genetic expression to exercise, attitude and mood, contemplative practice, stress management, and social and relational networks.

The medical culture is moving more toward health creation, prevention, and early detection of disease. As this occurs, our lifestyle choices and skills will be further called into play. At the Institute for Health & Healing, at California Pacific Medical

Center in San Francisco, we have developed "TLC"—
the Therapeutic Lifestyle Change Program—for
metabolic syndrome and other conditions. This
program is a vehicle to personalize and apply the
wealth of available health-related information in
ways that are practical, meaningful, and sustainable.

In the TLC Program, which includes the Four
Pillars of Self-Care (nutrition, physical activity,
contemplative practice/stress management, and
relationship/communication/community), we teach
and support people in making changes that are
compatible with the recommendations of health
experts and in alignment with each individual's
internal values, dreams, and desires.

Often, people participating in the TLC Program
and seeking to make healthy lifestyle choices are not
motivated to change their ways because the benefits
or consequences of their behavior seem remote from
their present circumstances. For example, if I quit
smoking will it really prevent lung cancer or
emphysema? If I change my diet will it really
forestall heart disease in the future? If I reduce my
level of stress will I be more content and as secure?

All health-creating change demands many daily,
even momentary, decisions be made that serve our
long-term interests. But they must serve our short-
term interests as well, so that positive results and
benefits are quickly experienced. In the TLC
Program, these early rewards and results (such as
enhanced sense of well-being, joy at doing what is
right, weight loss, lower blood pressure, improved
laboratory values) then become motivation for
further progress.

Getting in touch with our innermost longings
and wisdom is an essential part of maximizing our
capacity to change. To be in touch with our inner

world requires our slowing down, being quiet and paying full attention to that which is calling to us from within. It is only through our dedicated self-exploration, self-regulation, and self-care that we can sustain the internal authority and will power that will keep us true to our desired path. This is a lifelong process that requires repeated decisions that serve our best interest in the deepest sense. These decisions can't simply keep us in our comfort zone or in contact with what seems safe and familiar, or they will often perpetuate bad habits rather than lead us to the possibility of real growth and progress.

In this small-step by small-step way, TLC participants make choices and changes that move them away from ingrained patterns of undesired behavior (bad habits) toward that which serves their longer term best interests and supports their life dreams (e.g., meaningful work and relationships, compassionate service, long life). With small, doable increments, we bring results and consequences into close proximity with desired behavior change. This makes the whole change process more appealing and potentially successful and sustainable.

Inspiration can get us started, but results sustain our motivation. Over time, we create a daily practice—good habits—that gradually improves our physical well-being, raises our consciousness, and propels us to reach our goals. We become aware beings moving toward our true self-realization, be it our optimal genetic expression or our deepest held dreams.

That movement is *deep medicine* and will reward us with health, peace, and freedom.

# Afterword References

Bland, J.S., Benum, S.H. (1999). *Genetic Nutritioneering: How You Modify Inherited Traits and Live a Longer, Healthier Life*, Los Angeles, Keats Publishing.

Browner, WS, et al, "The Genetics of Human Longevity," *Am J Med.* 2004; 117:851–860.

Iyengar, B.K.S. (2005). *Light on Life: The Yoga Journey to Wholeness, Inner Peace, and Ultimate Freedom.* U.S.A.: Rodale Books.

*Newsweek*, "Diet and Genes: The New Science of Nutritional Aging," January 17, 2005.

*Newsweek*, "Stress and Your Heart," October 3, 2005.

Mark, S. et al, "Impact of the Metabolic Syndrome on Mortality from Coronary Heart Disease, Cardiovascular Disease, And All Causes In United States Adults," *Circulation.* 2004; 110: 1239–1244.

"Preventing Cancer, Cardiovascular Disease, and Diabetes: A Common Agenda for the American Cancer Society, the American Diabetes Society, and the American Heart Association," *Circulation.* 2004; 109:3244-3255.

# Appendix

## *Deep Medicine*
## Readings and References

*On my own path, I have drawn frequently from the works listed here. I am deeply grateful to the many teachers who have influenced my life. I apologize for any sources not properly acknowledged. Many of the authors listed have excellent CDs and tapes that further advance their work and extend their wisdom and teachings.*

Achterberg, Jeanne. (1990). *Woman as Healer.* Boston: Shambhala.

Anderson, Robert A. (2001). *A Clinician's Guide to Holistic Medicine.* New York: Hazelden/McGraw-Hill.

Anderson, Robert A, (1987). *Wellness Medicine.* Lynnwood, WA: American Health Press.

Annas, George J. (1995). "Reframing the Debate on Health Care Reform by Replacing our Metaphors," *New England Journal of Medicine* 332, (11); 745–748.

Arrien, Angeles. (1993). *The Four-Fold Way.* San Francisco: Harper.

Arrien, Angeles. (2005). *Second Half of Life.* Boulder, CO: Sounds True.

Arrien, Angeles. (2000). *The Nine Muses: A Mythological Path to Creativity.* New York: Tarcher/Putnam.

Arrien, Angeles. (1992). *Signs of Life.* Sonoma, CA: Araus Publishing Co.

Arrien, Angeles. (2000). *Update: In the Four-Fold Way Newsletter.* Fall-Winter.

Artress, Lauren. (1995). *Walking a Sacred Path: Rediscovering the Labyrinth as a Spiritual Tool.* New York: Riverhead Books.

Astin, John. (1998). "Why Patients Use Alternative Medicine." *Journal of the American Medical Association* 279, (11); 1896–7.

Balch, J., Balch P. (1997). *Prescription for Nutritional Healing.* Garden City Park, NY: Avery Publishing Group.

Baker, D., Stauth, C. (2002). *What Happy People Know: How the New Science of Happiness Can Change Your Life for the Better.* USA: Rodale Books.

Barks, Coleman. (trans.). (1995). *The Essential Rumi.* San Francisco: Harper.

Basu, S. (2000). *Integral Health: A Consciousness Approach to Health & Healing.* Pondicherry, India: Sri Aurobindo Ashram Press.

Bolen, Jean Shinoda. (1996). *Close to the Bone.* New York: Scribner.

Boorstein, Sylvia. (1996). *Don't Just Do Something, Sit There.* San Francisco: Harper.

Bridges, William. (1980). *Transitions.* New York: Addison-Wesley.

Cameron, J. (1992). *The Artist's Way: A Spiritual Path to Higher Creativity.* New York: Jeremy P. Tarcher/Putnam.

Capra, Fritjof. (1984). *The Tao of Physics,* New York: Bantam Books.

Chodron, Pema. (1994). *Start Where You Are.* Boston: Shambhala.

Chodron, Pema. (1991). *The Wisdom of No Escape.* Boston: Shambhala.

Chopra, Deepak. (1989). *Quantum Healing.* New York: Bantam Books.

Coelho, Paulo. (1995). *The Pilgrimage*. San Francisco: Harper.

Coelho, Paulo. (1998). *The Alchemist*. New York: HarperCollins, 1998.

Cousineau, Phil. (1998). *The Art of Pilgrimage*. Berkeley, CA: Conari Press.

Dalai Lama (HH), Howard C. Cutler. (1998). *The Art of Happiness*. New York: Riverhead Books.

Dass, Ram. (2000). *Still Here*. New York: Riverhead Books.

Dossey, Larry. (1999). *Reinventing Medicine*. San Francisco: Harper.

Douillard, J. (1994). *Body, Mind and Spirit: The Mind-Body Guide to Lifelong Fitness and Your Personal Best*. New York: Crown.

Fox, Matthew. (1991). *The Coming of the Cosmic Christ*. New York: Harper and Row.

Gallia, Katherine. (2001). "America's Healthiest Hospitals," *Natural Health*, December 2001.

Gardner, John W. (1995). *Self Renewal: The Individual and the Innovative Society*. New York: W.W. Norton & Co.

Geoff, D. (1998). "The Social Koan: Through Diversity to Interdependence," in Arrien, A. (ed) *Working Together: Producing Synergy by Honoring Diversity*. Pleasanton, CA: New Leaders Press.

Golan, Ralph. (1995). *Optimal Wellness*. New York: Ballantine Books.

Golden, Harry. (1958). *Only in America*. Cleveland: World Publishing.

Gordon, James. (1996). *Manifesto for a New Medicine*. Reading, MA: Addison-Wesley.

Gibran, K. (1989). *The Prophet*. New York: Alfred A. Knopf.

Hobson, Charles. (1999). *Human Touch: Images for a Garden*. San Francisco: Pacific Editions.

Irving, John. (1978). *The World According to Garp*.
New York: E.P.Dutton.

Iyengar, B.K.S. (2001). *Yoga: The Path to Holistic Health*. London: Dorling Kindersley Ltd.

Kabat-Zinn, J. (1990). *Full Catastrophic Living*. New York: Dell Publishing.

Kabat-Zinn, J. (1994). *Wherever You Go There You Are*. New York: Hyperion.

Kenny, D.K. (2002). *Promise of the Soul*. New York: John Wiley and Sons.

Kesten, D. (2001). *The Healing Secrets of Food*. Novato, CA: New World Library.

Keyes, K., Jr. (1985). *The Hundredth Monkey*. Coos Bay, Oregon: Vision Books.

Kleinman, A., Eisenberg, D., Good, B. (1978). "Culture, Illness, and Care: Clinical Lessons from Anthropologic and Cross Cultural Research." *Annals of Internal Medicine* (88); 251–258.

Kornfield, Jack. (1993). *A Path with Heart*. New York: Bantam Books.

Kornfield, J., Feldman, C. (1996). *Soul Food*. San Francisco: Harper.

Kushner, Lawrence. (1990). *The River of Light*. Woodstock, New York: Jewish Lights Publishing.

Kroenke, K. and Mangelsdorf, A.D. (1989). "Common Symptoms in Ambulatory Care: Incidence, Evaluation, Therapy and Outcome." *American Journal of Medicine*, 86; 262–266.

Lasater, Judith, et al. (2000). *Living Your Yoga: Finding the Spiritual in Everyday Life*. Berkeley, California: Rodell Press.

Levine, S. Levine, O. (1982). *Who Dies?* New York: Anchor Books/Doubleday.

Liester, M.B. (1996). "Inner Voices: Distinguishing Transcendent and Pathological Characteristics." *Journal of Transpersonal Psychology*, 28.

Longaker, Christine. (1997). *Facing Health and Finding Hope*. New York: Doubleday.

Lovelock, J. and Thomas, L. (1988). *The Ages of Gaia*. New York: Norton.

May, Rollo. (1975). *The Courage to Create*. New York: W.W. Norton. & Co.

Meade, Michael. (2005). *Fate and Destiny: The Eye of the Pupil, the Heart of the Disciple*. CD Set. Seattle: Mosaic Voices.

Meade, Michael. (2005). *Fate and Destiny: The Two Agreements*. CD Set. Seattle: Mosaic Voices.

Meyers, N., ed. (1984). *Gaia: An Atlas of Planet Management*. New York: Anchor Books.

Miller, W., Rollnick, S. (2002). *Motivational Interviewing: Preparing People for Change (2nd ed.)*. New York: Guilford Press.

Miller, W.R., deBaca, J.C. (1994). "Quantum Change: Toward a Psychology of Transformation." In *Can Personality Change*? Ed. by T. Heatheron and J. Weinberger, 253–280. Washington, D.C.: American Psychological Association.

Mitchell, Stephen,(trans.). (1992). *Tao Te Ching*. New York: Harper Perennial/HarperCollins.

Muller, Wayne. (1996). *How Then Shall We Live*. New York: Bantam Books.

Muller, Wayne. (1999). *Sabbath: Restoring the Sacred Rhythm of Rest*. New York: Bantam Books.

Murray, M., Pizzzorno, J. (1998). *Encyclopedia of Natural Medicine*. Rocklin, CA: Prima Publishing.

Myss, Caroline. (1997). *Why People Don't Heal and How They Can*. New York: Harmony Books

Northrup, Christine. (1998). *Women's Bodies, Women's Wisdom*. New York: Bantam Books

O'Donohue, John. (1998). *Anam Cara: A Book of Celtic Wisdom*. New York: Cliff Street Books (HarperCollins)

O'Donohue, John. (1999). *Eternal Echoes: Exploring Our Yearning to Belong.* New York: Cliff Street Books (HarperCollins)

Oman, Maggie,ed. (1997). *Prayers for Healing.* Berkeley, CA: Conari Press

O'Neil, Gisela and George. (1990). *The Human Life.* Spring Valley, New York: Mercury Press

Ornish, Dean. (1993). *Eat More, Weigh Less.* New York: HarperCollins

Ornish, Dean. (1998). *Love and Survival.* New York: HarperCollins

Pelletier, Kenneth. (2000). *The Best Alternative Medicine: What Works? What Does Not?* New York: Simon & Schuster

*Principles of Ecology.* Berkeley, California: Center of Ecoliteracy.

Remen, Rachel Naomi. (1996). *Kitchen Table Wisdom.* New York: Riverhead Books

Remen, Rachel Naomi. (2000). My *Grandfather's Blessings.* New York: Riverhead Books

Roszak, Theodore. (1992). *The Voice of the Earth.* New York: Simon & Schuster

Sapolsky, R.M. (2001). *Why Zebras Don't Get Ulcers: An Updated Guide to Stress, Stress-Related Diseases and Coping.* New York: N.H. Freeman and Co.

Scherwitz, L., Stewart, W., McHenry, P., Wood, C., Robertson, L., Cantwell, M. (August 2004). "A Descriptive Analysis of an Integrative Medicine Clinic." *The Journal of Alternative and Complementary Medicine: (651–659).*

Schiller, David, ed. (1994). *The Little Zen Companion.* New York: Workman Publishing.

Sears, Barry and Bill Lawren. (1995). *The Zone.* New York: HarperCollins.

Siegel, Bernie. (1988). *Love, Miracles and Medicine.*
New York: Harper and Row.

Simopoulos, Artemis P. and Jo Robinson. (1999).*The
Omega Diet.* New York: Harper Perennial.

Sobel, David and Ornstein, Robert. (1996). *The Healthy
Mind, Healthy Body Handbook.* Los Altos: DRx.

Sogyal, Rinpoche. (1992). *The Tibetan Book of Living
and Dying.* San Francisco: HarperCollins, 1992.

Spiegel, David. (1993). *Living Beyond Limits.* New York
Times Books/Random House.

Stewart, William B. (November/December 1988).
"Bearing Witness to the Evolution of Contemporary
Medicine: The Institute for Health & Healing at
California Pacific Medical Center, San Francisco."
*Healthcare Forum Journal*: 38–40.

Stewart, William B. (1994). "Health Care:
Transformation of Systems and Soul." *The Western
Journal of Medicine* 160: 273–274.

Stewart, William B. (June/July 2000). "The Institute for
Health & Healing: Contributing to the Evolution of
Contemporary Medicine." *San Francisco Medicine*:
18–20.

Stewart, William B., in Faass, N. (ed). (2001).
*Integrating Complementary Medicine Into Health
Systems.* Gaithersburg, Maryland: Aspen
Publishers: 406–411.

Stewart, William B. (May 2002). "The Labyrinth: A
Metaphoric Path to Health and Healing." *San
Francisco Medicine*: 23–25.

Stewart, William B. (1991). "Physician Heal Thy Planet."
*The Western Journal of Medicine.* 155: 538–539.

Stewart, William B. (2000). "Surgery, Service and Soul."
*Ophthalmic Plastic and Reconstructive Surgery.*
16, No. 6: 401–406.

Stewart, William B. (1993). "Way of the Healer—The Work of Healing and the Healing of Work." *The Western Journal of Medicine*. 158:629–630.

Saint-Exupéry, Antoine de. (1943/1971). *The Little Prince*. San Diego/New York: Harcourt Brace.

Stone, D, Patton B., Heen, S. (2000). *Difficult Conversations: How to Discuss What Matters Most*. New York: Penguin Books.

Sun Tzu. (1991). *The Art of War*. Translated by Thomas Cleary. Boston: Shambhala.

Swimme, Brian and Berry, Thomas. (1992). *The Universe Story*. San Francisco: Harper.

Thich Nhat Hanh. (1987). *The Miracle of Mindfulness*. Boston: Beacon Press.

Thomas, Lewis. (1974). *Lives of a Cell*. New York: Viking Press.

Thurston, Mark. (1987). *Paradox of Power*. Virginia Beach: A.R.E. Press.

Thurston, Mark. (1989). *Soul Purpose*. New York: St. Martin's Press.

Thurston, Mark. (2001). *Twelve Positive Habits of Spiritually Centered People*. Virginia Beach: A.R.E. Press.

Tolle, Eckhart. (1999). *The Power of Now: A Guide to Spiritual Enlightenment*. Novato, CA: New World Library.

Venkataswamy, Govindappa. (1994). *Illuminated Spirit*. New York: Paulist Press.

Watson, Lyall. (1980). *Lifetide*. New York: Simon & Schuster.

Watts, Alan. (1951). *The Wisdom of Insecurity*. New York: Vintage Books/Random House.

Webb, Wyatt. (2002). *It's Not About The Horse—It's About Overcoming Fear and Self-Doubt*. Carlsbad, CA: Hay House.

Weil, Andrew. (1997). 8 *Weeks to Optimum Health*. New York: Alfred A. Knopf.

Weil, Andrew. (2005). *Healthy Aging*. New York: Alfred A. Knopf.

White, T.P. (1993). *The Wellness Guide to Lifelong Fitness*. New York: Rebus.

Wilber, Ken. (2000). *The Theory of Everything*. Boston: Shambhala.

Zukav, Gary. (1989). *The Dancing Wu Li Masters*. New York: Bantam Books.

# About the Author

William B. Stewart is the Medical Director of the Institute for Health & Healing at the California Pacific Medical Center (CPMC), in San Francisco, and Marin General Hospital, in Greenbrae, California. He is the past Chair of the Department of Ophthalmology and a member of the Senior Management Team at CPMC.

After graduating from the University of Minnesota Medical School in 1968, Dr. Stewart completed his internship at the University of Colorado. He then had a year of general surgery training at the University of California, San Francisco, and a two-year tour of duty in the Medical Corps of the U.S. Air Force. He received ophthalmology residency training at CPMC and his fellowship training at the University of London Moorfields Eye Hospital and the University of Miami/Bascom Palmer Eye Institute. Returning to the Bay Area in 1977, he joined the Department of Ophthalmology at CPMC as Director of Ophthalmic Plastic, Reconstructive, and Orbital Surgery. He became the Department Chair in 1996 and served in that capacity until 2000.

He has lectured nationally and internationally, from India to Israel and Maine to Montana, and is the author of many scientific publications and thought-provoking commentaries.

Dr. Stewart has been on the Best Doctors in America list since its inception in 1989. He has also been honored by inclusion in the *Best Doctors in the San Francisco Bay Area*.

In 1989, influenced by a lifelong interest in philosophy and medical work at the Aravind Eye Hospital in India, Dr. Stewart participated in the creation of what is today the Institute for Health & Healing. His vision and work merge the scientific and the sacred, engaging in a deep and broad comprehension of the nature of healing.

He is a longtime student of, and mentor for, the work of Angeles Arrien, cultural anthropologist, educator, and specialist in comparative religion and philosophy. He uses her teachings in his healing work.

Dr. Stewart is married and lives in Muir Beach, California. His wife Susy is a consultant to the Mill Valley, California, School District, an environmental educator, student, and teacher of yoga—an enduring inspiration and sustaining partner. They have two grown sons and, since the birth of their grandchildren, have a broader and deeper perspective on the cycles of life and the principles and practices of mindful living and lifelong learning.

For more information about *Deep Medicine*, Dr. Stewart, or the Institute for Health & Healing, contact:

| | |
|---|---|
| E-mail: | cpmcihh@sutterhealth.org |
| Telephone: | (415) 600-HEAL (4325) |
| Fax: | (415) 600-3645 |
| Website: | www.myhealthandhealing.org |
| Mail: | **Institute for Health & Healing** |
| | California Pacific Medical Center |
| | P.O. Box 7999 |
| | San Francisco, CA 94120-7999 |